KU-167-455

fish & figs

the world's healthiest recipes from the island of crete

Notes
1 Standard level spoon measurements are used in all the recipes.
1 tablespoon = one 15 ml spoon
1 teaspoon = one 5 ml spoon

2 Both imperial and metric measurements have been given in all recipes. Use one set of measurements only and not a mixture of both.

3 Eggs should be medium unless otherwise stated. The Department of Health advises that eggs should not be consumed raw. This book contains dishes made with raw or lightly cooked eggs. It is prudent for more vulnerable people such as pregnant and nursing mothers, invalids, the elderly, babies and young children to avoid uncooked or lightly cooked dishes made with eggs. Once prepared, these dishes should be kept refrigerated and used promptly.

4 Milk should be full fat unless otherwise stated.

5 Fresh herbs should be used unless otherwise stated. If unavailable, use dried herbs as an alternative but halve the quantities stated. Pepper is freshly ground black pepper.

6 Ovens should be preheated to the specified temperature – if using a fan assisted oven, follow the manufacturer's instructions for adjusting the time and the temperature.

Catherine Serbource-Madani
was assisted by Mika Shimpo in the book design

Conception and production: Corinne Pauvert Thiounn

Cover: Guylaine and Christophe Moi

Cover photos:
Top: Pierre Hussenot
Bottom: E. Slatter/Hemispheres
Back cover: Pierre Cabannes

Publishing Secretary: Sylvie Gauthier

Editorial: Caroline Rolland

First published by Hachette Pratique, an imprint of Hachette-Livre
43 Quai de Grenelle, Paris 75905, Cedex 15, France
© 2000, Hachette Pratique – Hachette-Livre
Under the title Bienfaits et Délices du Régime Crétois
All rights reserved.

American English translation © 2002, Ici La Press, Connecticut
British English adaptation produced by Translate-A-Book, Oxford

© 2003, British English Text, Octopus Publishing Group Ltd, London
This edition published by Hachette Illustrated UK, Octopus Publishing Group,
2–4 Heron Quays, London, E14 4JP

Printing and binding by Toppan in China

ISBN 1-84430-006-4

fish & figs

the world's healthiest recipes from the island of crete

for vitality, health and longevity

Jacques Fricker
Dominique Laty

Photography by
Pierre Hussenot and
Pierre Cabannes

Design by
Catherine Serbource-Madani

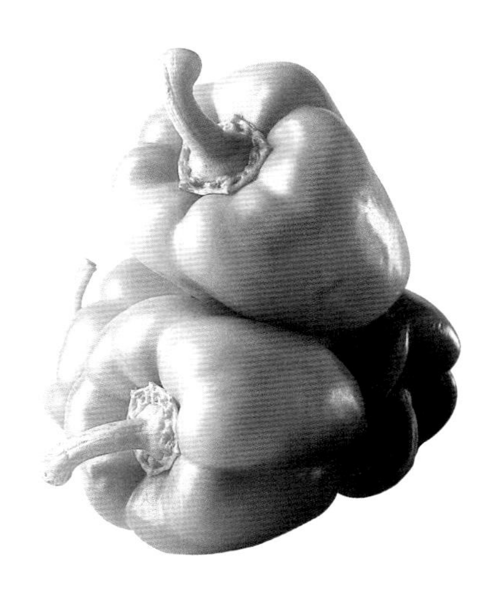

foreword

Today we live longer, but is the quality of our life better? Consider the tremulous rhythm of life, the stress we bear and the undisciplined manner in which we often feed our bodies with too much fat and refined sugar. All these factors have serious consequences on us as human beings. With this in mind, we have, within the last few years, been driven to look for a different, healthier diet – and a saner, more reasonable way of eating. The Cretan method, which combines gastronomy and the art of living, reflects this more healthy model.

The Cretan principles are simple and unchanging. Every day, you should eat bread, cereals, fruit, fresh vegetables, pulses, cheese or yogurt and olives; cook the food in, and season it with, olive oil; drink plenty of water and a little red wine several times a week; eat fish, chicken, eggs and sweet desserts several times a week; and enjoy red meat only three or four times a month.

This diet is the key to a longer life and promotes good health. These benefits were observed by travellers as early as the eighteenth century and were later corroborated by scientific discoveries. In the 1950s, American researcher Ancel Keys concluded that the Cretans' longevity was a direct result of their diet, which was clearly superior to the diet of both the Japanese and the Americans. More recently, Frenchman Serge Renaud confirmed Keys' conclusions when he adapted certain principles of the Cretan system to the meals he served to a group of his patients who were suffering from heart problems.

Convinced by the above observations and research, we offer in this book some of our Cretan recipes, which were inspired by the products of our land, our present way of life, simplicity, rapidity and the pleasure of taste. These recipes will point you in the right direction for good living, or *regimen*, the Latin word which meant, early on, a general manner of living. To adopt these recipes is to put 'health on your plate'.

contents

Behind the Mégaron
were found the treasures:
jars in which wheat,
barley, vegetables, oil,
and figs were
conserved from
one harvest to another.

Paul Faure, *Ulysse le Crétois*

Harmony and simplicity

A brilliant civilization began in Crete, a small Mediterranean island, in the eleventh century BC and reached its summit between 1700 and 1400 BC. The palaces, of which the most famous is the palace of Knossos and the seat of the legendary dynasty of Minos, date from this era. Surviving vestiges include frescoes that are evidence of the court life – the religious rituals and the lavish celebrations of a dynasty very involved in earthly pleasures. Thanks to the considerable power enjoyed by the king and to a writing system (Linear A) which allowed him to centralize and co-ordinate commercial activity, Crete developed trade with Egypt and the Cyclades and spread its maritime domination over the whole Aegean Sea. A century later, Crete lost its power; henceforth, the model of the Hellenic city would be concentrated within the confines of the island. It became a Roman colony before coming under Arabic, Venetian (until the end of the seventeenth century) and then Turkish and Greek domination. Many influences inspired Cretan cuisine without its ever losing its uniqueness.

A local production of quality

The face of Crete is marked by the presence of massive mountains broken by a few plains and hills. This geographical variety is reflected in its local agriculture: the rearing of sheep, pigs and goats is concentrated on the arid sides of the mountains; the cultivation of olive trees, fig trees and vines takes place on the hills; and the production of cereals (barley) and vegetables (cucumbers, courgettes, fennel and radishes) occurs

This face, weathered by the years, could by itself symbolize Crete - a Mediterranean island where the population, which strongly adheres to its traditions and dietary principles, attains an amazing longevity.

The massive mountainous slopes easily adapt to the rearing of goats and sheep. They also enable the harvesting of wild and aromatic herbs which add flavour and nutrients to the diet.

mostly on the plains. Some of this produce has, for centuries, competed for the top position, indeed, for the wealth of the island. Olive oil and wine have never lost their pre-eminence with the passing of time, nor have aromatics, such as fennel, coriander, cumin and aniseed, cultivated as early as the Minoan era.

Cretans like simple but savoury cooking. Eating is most of all an excuse to share pleasure with friends. Frugality and the search for the harmony of the body constitute the characteristics of Cretan civilization, as testified to by images of fighting women, bullfighters and figures somersaulting over the horns of a bull, depicted on a vase rediscovered at the time of the excavations of the Hagia Triad site. Cretan customs have changed very little since antiquity. Because of its island location, Crete has remained protected, despite invasions and colonization during the course of history, from radical changes or the stress endemic in other countries. Its only concession to modernity is the introduction of citrus fruits and the cultivation of tomatoes in winter. If yesterday's shepherd has become today's farmer, he continues to cook the same dishes using the superb produce of the island.

The Cretan table

There are four basic, essential elements to the Cretan diet – olive oil, octopus, snails and *vlita*, a vegetable called 'African spinach' by the Chinese, which is boiled and served with lemon, olive oil, potatoes and courgettes. Part of any meal is the ever-present bread, usually similar to a galette, a broad, thin cake, dried in the oven – related to the French fougasse. Seventy-two varieties (at last count) of the bread are made with a range of cereals, cooked in different ways – with or without yeast, with poppy seeds, cumin seeds, aniseed, sage, capers, garlic, onion, olives, grapes, milk or olive oil.

The basic ingredients for Cretan cuisine are a variety of vegetables, including peppers, chard, radishes, fennel – both the leaves and bulbs – potatoes, aubergines, dandelions (*radika*) and artichokes (*stamnangathia*), which grow in the wild. Add to that pulses, such as chickpeas, *gesses* or black peas, *vesces* or yellow peas, pigeon or gunga peas, broad beans, kidney beans and lentils. Whether fresh or dried, vegetables and pulses form the basis of Cretan salads and they are seasoned with various herbs and spices – oregano, cumin, mint, rosemary, parsley, dill, basil, celery, cinnamon and sage – as well as, of course, garlic and onions. Besides the traditional peasant salad (*salata horiatiki*), cucumber with yogurt (*tzatziki*), or green beans with oil (*fassolada*), the meal can include vine leaves stuffed with rice (*dolmadakia*), puréed chickpeas (*houmus*) or sesame oil (*tahini*). A piece of cheese (*bougatsa*) or some walnuts will satisfy a small appetite.

The sea has always been a source of wealth, providing Cretans with an abundance and great variety of fish, some of which are represented by the paintings on the sarcophagi or walls of Minoan palaces.

Traditionally, Cretans eat red mullet, grey mullet, sea bass, scorpion fish, bonito, whiting, sardines and swordfish. Anchovies are served as a side dish accompanied by a bean salad. Cretans also value sea bream, whether it is emperor (*tsipoura*), red (*fagri*) or grey (*sargos*). Tuna, fresh or canned, is appreciated, especially in salads, and sole is fried in olive oil. Cretans are equally fond of small,

The remains of Knossos palace (here, the sacred Temple) are witness to the grandeur of the Minoan civilization that had its peak about 1700–1400 BC.

The excavations of Knossos revealed magnificent frescoes. One of the most famous is a painting of dolphins in the queen's chambers.

For centuries, Crete, because of its island location, knew how to preserve a high-quality lifestyle and a healthy diet. Tourism, which has been rampant for several decades (Crete is the most sought-after Greek island destination), has had some influence on the Cretan diet.

Bordering both the Mediterranean Sea and the Aegean Sea, Crete enjoys an unlimited supply of saltwater fish, including red mullet, grey mullet, sea bass, sea bream, bonito, sardines, swordfish and anchovies.

It is difficult to imagine Greece and its islands without the olive tree. In antiquity, olive oil was the main source of wealth and a vital, necessary product. Not only was it a significant part of cooking, it was also a source of light and body care, used in ointments and perfumes. The connoisseurs of oil, from Praisos, Gournia, Malia, and Vathipetro, testify that during the Minoan era, the search for high-quality olive oil was already a constant preoccupation.

Local produce reflects the diversity of the landscape - farming on the slopes of the mountains, olive trees and vineyards on the hills, grains and vegetables on the plains.

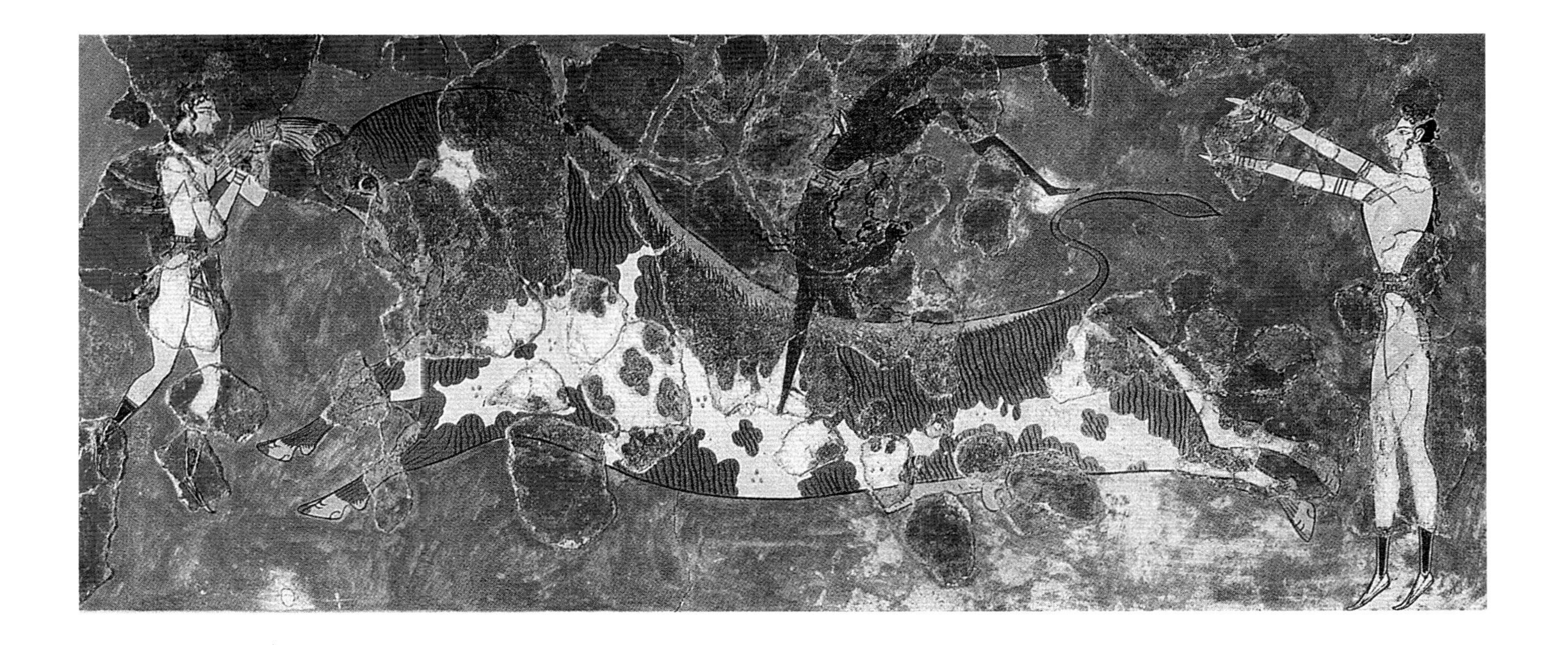

grey snails, prepared in a sauce with tomatoes, potatoes and onions (*stifado hochlious*), and of sea urchins, crabs and winkles. They also feast on octopus or *oktapodi*, which they catch with a trident, the *kamaki,* and on small squid cooked in batter (*kalamarakia*).

In ancient times, meat from donkeys, horses, peacocks, water fowl, foxes and hedgehogs was served on the elegant royal table. Nevertheless, meat remains an occasional dish. When Cretans do eat meat, it is most often lamb or roasted, aromatic chicken accompanied by fresh vegetables or in kebabs sprinkled with lemon (*souvlaki*), spiced meatballs (*keftedes*), small sticks of minced meat fried and served with an onion sauce, tomatoes and peppers (*souzoukakia*) or *pastitsio*, a kind of macaroni cheese with minced meat, tomatoes, cheese and béchamel sauce – a testimony to the 400 years of Venetian occupation. It is likely that the meal would consist of either a goat fricassée with cheese, green vegetables and fennel or a rabbit stew, seasoned with fresh orange juice, bay leaves and cloves (*stifado*).

Cheeses are made from the milk of both sheep and goats and curdled with fig juice. *Mizithra* goat's cheese, similar to ricotta, is eaten fresh or dry and used in tarts, while feta, a crumbly, white ewe's milk cheese, goes well with a melon or watermelon salad flavoured with mint – a welcome treat after a siesta. Yogurts, whose consistency is close to crème fraîche, are used mainly to make sauces, but they are also eaten alone, sweetened with a little honey.

Kalitsounia, a cheesecake made with fresh ewe's milk cheese, is served at Easter – like other cakes, it is served only on holidays and very special occasions. Cakes demonstrate the Turkish and Arab influence on Crete – baklava, fritters with honey (*loukoumades*) and biscuits fried in olive oil and covered with honey syrup, cinnamon, walnuts and cloves (*xaratigana*).

The Knossos palace walls are decorated with mosaics, witnesses of a rich civilization. This somersault above a bull evokes as much a taste for athletic exploits as a ritual.

This Iraklion merchant is drying nuts in the sun – nuts rich in protective nutrients and high in calories.

During a meal, Cretans quench their thirst with water and a fruity red wine, which is aged, sometimes for years, in earthen jars and whose tannins possess an antioxidant property. Four local wines deserve recognition – *archanes*, *peza*, *dasnes* and *sitia*. Raki, a white grape spirit, is consumed during all the occasions that give rhythm to life on the island. Several towns organize parties around their agricultural year. They celebrate the chestnut harvest in Hania and grape picking in Sitia where the *sultanine* (grape harvest) takes place every year between August 19 and 22.

Coffee is served at the end of the meal. Prepared the Turkish way, it is served without sugar (*sketo*), not very sweet (*metrio*) or very sweet (*gliko*).

Several times a year, Cretans observe a period of abstinence – Lent, the 40 days that precede Easter, the days preceding Christmas, as well as August 1 to 15 (the feast of the Assumption). During these times, red meat is avoided. Both meat and poultry are replaced by eggs, fish, snails and shellfish.

Cretan food is simple food, with uncomplicated preparation enhancing the freshness and the natural qualities of the produce used. Traditional Cretan cuisine demonstrates that good eating can also mean good health.

The market stalls stimulate the senses of passers by. They offer a huge variety of vegetables, fruit and fish, which, today, are sometimes imported.

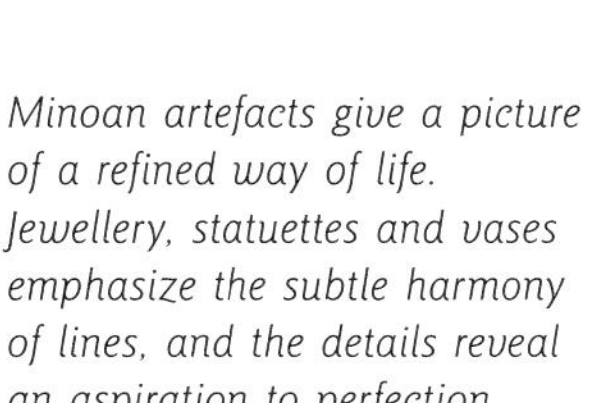

Minoan artefacts give a picture of a refined way of life. Jewellery, statuettes and vases emphasize the subtle harmony of lines, and the details reveal an aspiration to perfection.

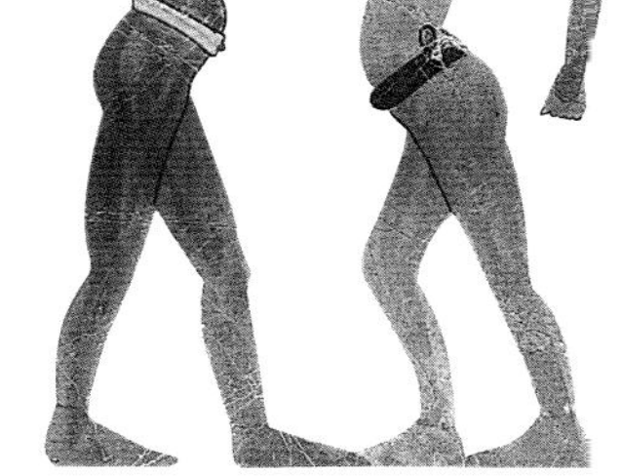

With its different wine-producing regions, Crete enjoys full-bodied wines which have beneficial effects. Crete is, without doubt, the protégé of Dionysus. Crete never hesitates to celebrate this god of wine every year with festivals and village holidays.

the benefits of cretan cooking

The massive growth in tourism has destabilized traditional Cretan life over the last 30 years. Eating a simple diet of fruit, bread and olive oil has yielded to the more profitable consumption of cheeses and meat. Having become aware of the consequences of their modern diet (with a notable increase in cardiovascular disease), today's young Cretans are rediscovering the virtues of their ancestors' diet. Now we are witnessing a return to abstinence and fasting as a reaction to the forces of modern nutrition. Paradoxically, 'the Cretan system' has become embedded in Crete once again.

When gastronomy and scientific research meet

Traditional Cretan cooking rests on simple principles:

- Eat fruit, fresh vegetables, bread, cereal or dried pulses, cheese or yogurt and olives every day.
- Cook with olive oil and use it for salad and vegetable dressings.
- Drink plenty of water and a little red wine occasionally.
- Eat fish, chicken, eggs and desserts several times a week.
- Eat red meat only three or four times a month.

It is an appetizing way of serving food which has interested scientists for more than half a century. Why? Researchers, impressed with the exceptional longevity of Cretans, wanted to find the reason and discovered for themselves the benefits of Cretan cuisine.

In 1948 a team of American scientists was sent to Crete with the task of thoroughly observing the lifestyle, health and diet of every one of the 150 families living on the island. These scientists compared the diet of Cretans with that

Bread is traditionally a part of the Cretan diet (here, a bakery in Rethimno). Baked with several cereals and cooked in the shape of galettes, the loaves have different flavours – cumin seed, poppy seed, aniseed and olives. Don't be surprised if, in restaurants or tavernas, the price of bread is included in the bill.

Most Cretans are fishermen because of their proximity to the sea. Nevertheless, it is not unusual to meet a shepherd or a peasant in the countryside, relaxing in the shade of an olive tree. The bucolic scene reminds us that the Cretan diet is equally a way of life.

of Americans. They discovered that Cretans did not eat less fat than Americans, but that the source of fat was drastically different. In the United States, fats were largely of animal origin – meat, milk products, butter, eggs, pastries, ice creams, biscuits, etc. – whereas in Crete, nearly 80 per cent of fats came from olives and olive oil. Cretans also clearly ate more dried pulses and cereal products, especially bread, sources of vegetable proteins, and less meat, eggs and milk products. Most of all, Cretans consumed almost twice the quantity of fruit and vegetables eaten by Americans. Comparatively, the Cretans' health was, in general, excellent, except in very poverty-stricken households.

A few years later, in 1952, another study compared diet and its correlation to the risks of cardiovascular diseases in seven countries – the United States, Finland, Holland, Japan, Italy, Yugoslavia and Greece, differentiating from this last country the island of Corfu (situated between Italy and the Hellenic peninsula) and Crete (in the Aegean Sea, to the extreme south of the archipelago of the Cyclades). This study specifically was going to follow the health of 100,000 individuals in these seven countries during more than 20 years – the effects of diet on the body usually take that long to appear. The results were very revealing, notably in regard to death by coronary disease and by heart attacks. In the 100,000 subjects studied, the death rate as a result of coronary disease was 50 times lower in Crete than in the United States or Finland. In Corfu and the other Mediterranean countries (Yugoslavia and Italy) and Japan, the number of deaths was less than in the United States but more than in Crete.

Furthermore, the study showed not only that Cretans have stronger hearts than the subjects in the other countries, but also that the Cretans' general health

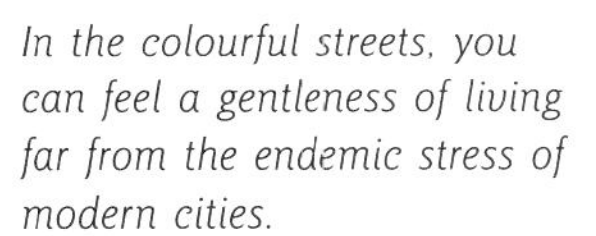
In the colourful streets, you can feel a gentleness of living far from the endemic stress of modern cities.

appeared to be miraculously protected. Mortality and all its causes considered in the 20 years of study was almost three times less in Crete than in Finland and half as much as in Italy or Japan. Cancer, for example, appeared half as often in Crete as in Italy, Holland or Finland. Cretans were thus found to be in better health than their compatriots on the same continent, on the island of Corfu or again in Italy and Yugoslavia, even though all were equally significant consumers of olive oil, which is thought to have protective qualities for the heart and the arteries.

Therefore other dietary factors had to be considered in the Cretan exception. It is necessary to think about the Cretan lifestyle. It differs in many ways from that of people living in America or Finland. The rhythm, the pulse, is more relaxed in Crete. Daily siestas, the presence of sun and sea, a gentle climate and social habits may be factors that, theoretically, influence mental and physical health at the same time.

In the mid-1990s, a French scientist, Serge Renaud, conducted a study at Lyon's hospital in collaboration with a team of cardiovascular pathologists: 605 patients who had had a heart attack in the preceding months volunteered to test two types of diet in order to prevent a relapse. The first one corresponded to the classic diet that had been used in the United States and in France, which tried to lower patients' blood cholesterol levels by reducing the amount of animal fat intake and replacing it with fats from vegetables (sunflower or corn) without really taking into account any other aspects of nutrition. The second proposed regimen was very similar to the Cretan diet.

It very quickly became obvious that the second diet produced a greater decrease (about 75 per cent) in cardiac problems and at the same time reduced the frequency of cancers in that group. It proved that the Cretan system is particularly beneficial for the arteries, the heart and general health and that it constitutes one of the best, if not the very best diets for healthy living.

Cretan cooking for everyone

To eat the Cretan way, there are only three choices:

- Live in Crete, which would be a great pleasure but is not always possible.
- Buy all groceries from a speciality shop to enable the regular consumption of olive oil, octopus, snails and so on.
- Shop at your usual supermarket but buy only Cretan foods. This is the simplest and most efficient way to follow the Cretan diet.

To each his own plate . . . Cretan

To bring a Cretan touch would be universally beneficial, but it is not necessarily the same for everyone. Some periods of life and certain conditions have different health requirements.

Pregnancy, childhood, and adolescence

During adolescence, the body has an increased need for calcium and high-quality proteins because of the natural growth cycle. Never banish all foods of animal origin from your diet. Focus on fruit, vegetables and starches, but also eat meat, fish and especially dairy products, which are rich in calcium. This

WHERE DO THE CRETANS GET THEIR GOOD HEALTH?	IN WHICH FOODS DO THEY FIND THESE PROTECTIVE NUTRIENTS?	HOW TO BE AS HEALTHY IN BRITAIN?
Folic acid and vitamin C: beta carotene the flavonoids	A variety of foods and plenty of fruit and vegetables: garlic, onions, aromatic herbs	Eat vegetables with lunch and dinner and at least three portions of fruit a day
The nature of fatty acids: monounsaturated fats in larger quantities than saturated or polyunsaturated fats	Cooking based on olive oil	For salad dressings, use olive or rapeseed oil instead of the other oils, butter or cream
The fatty acids: omega-3	Fish and snails; some green vegetables, such as purslane; desserts based mainly on almonds or walnuts	Eat fish at least twice a week; choose oily varieties; use rapeseed oil regularly, sometimes walnut or soya oil; eat walnuts, almonds and other nuts
Calcium: the dairy yeast	Fermented cheeses or yogurt	Appreciate yogurt and cheese
The slow glucoses: folic acid, magnesium, phytolite acids	Dried pulses, pastas, couscous, bulgar wheat, semolina and rice; unrefined flour	Eat one of these foods at each meal
The proteins: oil – trace elements, such as iron, zinc and selenium; vitamin B_{12}	Poultry, meat or eggs, all in moderate frequency or quantity to avoid the consequences of excess	Eat poultry, meat and eggs but in moderation, especially red meat
Red wine: the polyphenols	Red wine with meals	Be aware of the harm of excessive consumption of alcohol
The pleasure of eating: conviviality	Choice of savoury foods; simple preparation; sharing meals with friends and relatives	For the pleasure of taste, try the following recipes; as for conviviality, do you really need any advice?

Garlic, onions and aromatic herbs:

garlic

dill

cumin

fennel seeds

bay

mint

onions

oregano

rosemary

sage

Protecting against oxidation and old age

All living cells are progressively altered because of the processes of oxidation, with the formation of harmful molecules called free radicals. In the human body, oxidation accelerates ageing and can encourage the development of some diseases such as cancer or cardiovascular irregularities. Food plays a preventative role with the presence of its antioxidant substances, especially vitamins C and E, as well as the polyphenols and carotene, also called pro-vitamin A. The Cretan diet is rich in these various protective elements, which are present in fruit, vegetables and aromatic herbs.

same advice is true for pregnant women and nursing mothers. For them, as for the child or the adolescent, the omega-3 fatty acids (in rapeseed oil, soya beans, nuts and oily fish) are particularly important for the formation and function of the neurons and, therefore, for the intellect.

Seniors

With age, the principal risk is not so much cardiovascular diseases, cancer or obesity, but malnutrition. If you appreciate the principles of the Cretan diet, you should adopt them – they will not only give you a good appetite but will also be beneficial to your health. However, do not drastically and suddenly change your eating habits, as you would risk disturbing a sometimes precarious balance.

After the age of 70, proteins from animal sources are particularly valuable in reducing the risks of muscular degeneration. Add the vegetable produce – starches, bread, oils, fruit and vegetables – proposed by the Cretan system, but also welcome meat and dairy products to your table.

Obesity

In spite of the ever-present olive oil, the Cretan diet does not give rise to increased weight problems thanks to the important role given to fruit and vegetables which balance the calorific intake of meals and keep the body in good physical shape. On the other hand, it does not reduce weight.

If you are trying to lose weight, reduce by half the quantity of oil recommended in the recipes included in this book, and eat starches for lunch or dinner, but not for both meals.

Cardiovascular problems

Whether you do or do not have a cardiovascular problem, the Cretan system will be beneficial for your arteries, especially if you have a tendency towards angina. This is also true if you have any risk of a cardiovascular disease (high cholesterol, diabetes, arterial hypertension, tobacco use or a sedentary lifestyle). If your parents or siblings have suffered, before the age of 65, from a cardiovascular disease, your risk is high and you would benefit from watching your nutrition.

Rich protective elements of fruits for health

Apricots:
rich in carotene;
flavonoids in
significant quantity

Pineapples:
rich in vitamin C

Avocados:
folic acid and
vitamin C in
significant quantity

Bananas:
vitamin C in
significant quantity

Plantains:
rich in vitamin C

Blackcurrants:
very rich in vitamin C;
flavonoids in
significant quantity

Cherries:
folic acid, vitamin C
and flavonoids in
significant quantity

Chestnuts:
rich in folic acid
and vitamin C

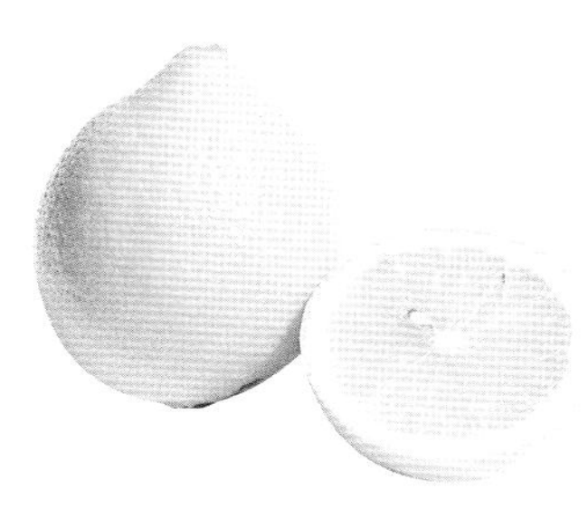

Lemons:
very rich in vitamin C

Tangerines:
very rich in vitamin C

Quinces:
vitamin C in
significant quantity

Fresh dates:
folic acid and
vitamin C in
significant quantity

Prickly pears:
rich in vitamin C

Figs:
rich in vitamin C

Strawberries:
rich in folic acid;
very rich in vitamin C

Raspberries:
folic acid and flavonoids in
significant quantity; rich in
vitamin C

Passion fruit:
rich in vitamin C

Rich protective elements of fruits for health

Guavas:
very rich in vitamin C

Pomegranates:
rich in vitamin C

Currants (red or white):
rich in vitamin C;
flavonoids in
significant quantity

Persimmons:
rich in carotene

Kiwi fruit:
folic acid in
significant quantity;
very rich in vitamin C

Mangoes:
folic acid in
significant quantity;
very rich in vitamin C;
rich in carotene

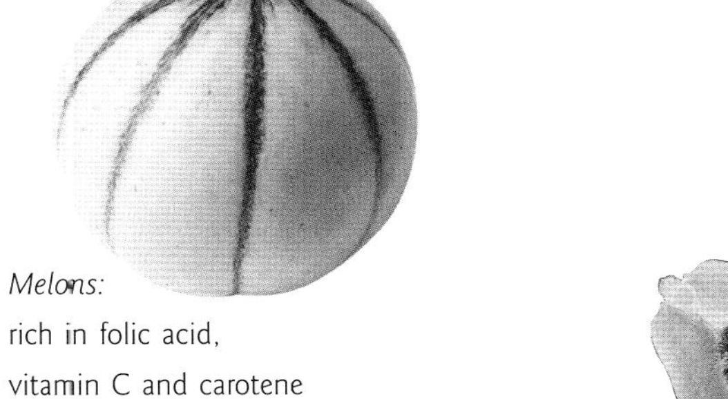

Melons:
rich in folic acid,
vitamin C and carotene

Blackberries:
rich in vitamin C;
flavonoids in
significant quantity

Blueberries:
rich in vitamin C;
flavonoids in
significant quantity

Oranges:
folic acid and flavonoids in
significant quantity;
very rich in vitamin C

Papayas:
folic acid
and carotene in
significant quantity;
very rich in vitamin C

Watermelons:
vitamin C in
significant quantity

Ruby grapefruit:
rich in vitamin C;
flavonoids in
significant quantity

Apples:
flavonoids in
significant quantity

Black grapes:
flavonoids in
significant quantity

Fruit and vegetables in large quantities

The importance of and the benefits provided by fruit and vegetables are taken for granted in the Cretan system. These ingredients contain many protective elements (see pages 26 and 30), such as carotene, vitamin C, or flavonoids, dietary fibre, potassium and magnesium – as, for example, the purslane's omega-3 essential fatty acids (see page 38).

It is recommended that you eat at least one vegetable and, if possible, several with each of the two principal meals, lunch and dinner, whether as a starter – raw vegetables or in a soup – or an accompaniment to the main dish. The vegetables may be cooked or raw; although it is better to eat a fresh raw vegetable or green salad at least once every other day to obtain an adequate supply of certain vitamins.

Heat often destroys vitamin C and folic acid. However, don't overlook cooked vegetables just because of this as they are often very tasty and increase variety in the presentation and flavour of dishes. Furthermore, cooked vegetables also have some benefits. Cooking tomatoes, for example, makes absorbing their protective antioxidant, lycopene, easier on the system. This is also true of red peppers.

As for fruit, eat whatever is in season, consuming at least two fresh fruits each day. Fruit is a delicious dessert, but makes a wonderful snack, too.

Finally, to optimize their general protective benefits, try to vary fruits and vegetables. Dried fruits are richer in energy than fresh fruits and they constitute a very good source of vitamins and magnesium. Walnuts, almonds and other nuts also provide the omega-3 fatty acids that protect the heart (see page 38).

Rich protective elements of vegetables for health

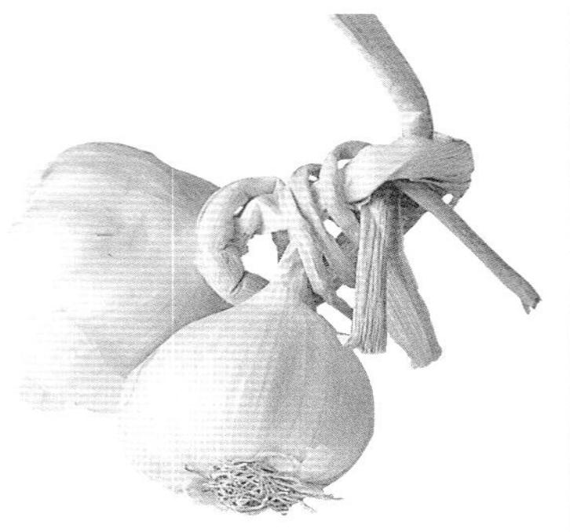

Garlic:
rich in vitamin C

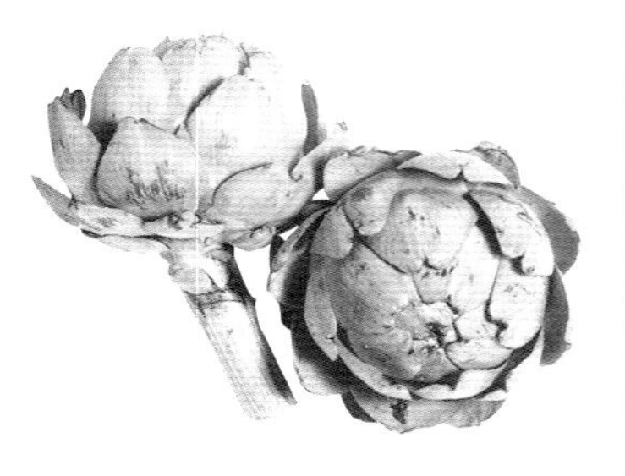

Globe artichokes:
folic acid and vitamin C in significant quantity

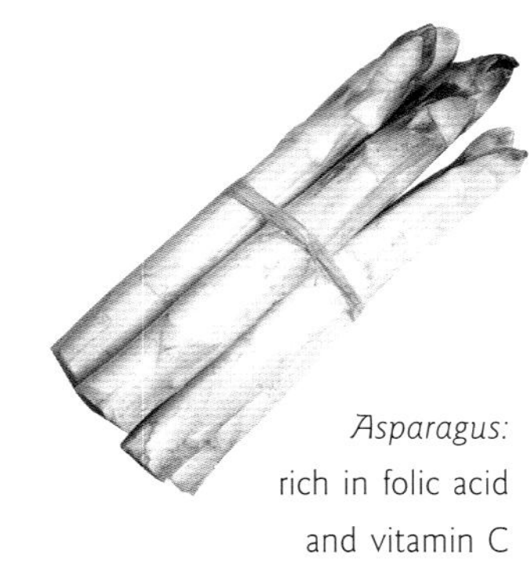

Asparagus:
rich in folic acid and vitamin C

Beetroot:
rich in folic acid; vitamin C in significant quantity

Celeriac:
folic acid, vitamin C and flavonoids in significant quantity

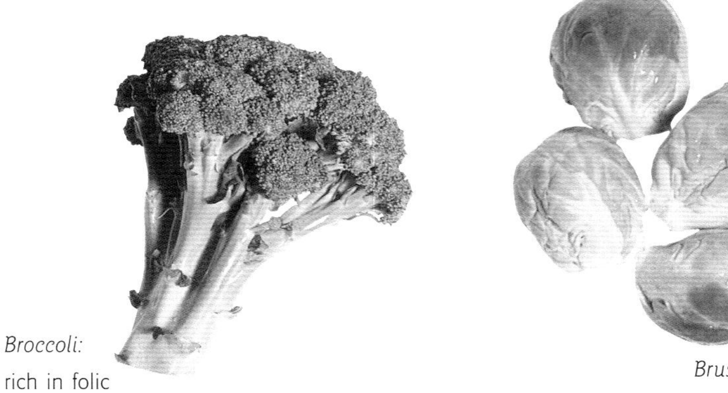

Broccoli:
rich in folic acid; very rich in vitamin C; carotene and flavonoids in significant quantity

Brussels sprouts:
rich in folic acid; very rich in vitamin C; flavonoids in significant quantity

Carrots:
folic acid and vitamin C in significant quantity; very rich in carotene

Cauliflower:
folic acid in significant quantity; very rich in vitamin C

Green cabbages:
rich in folic acid; very rich in vitamin C and carotene

Kale:
rich in flavonoids

Red cabbages:
folic acid in significant quantity; very rich in vitamin C

Spring onions:
rich in flavonoids

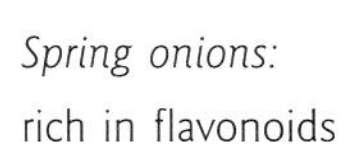

Cucumbers:
vitamin C in significant quantity

Pickled cucumbers:
carotene in significant quantity

Rich protective elements of vegetables for health

Courgettes:
folic acid in significant quantity; rich in vitamin C

Sea kale:
rich in folic acid and vitamin C

Watercress:
very rich in folic acid and vitamin C; rich in carotene

Chicory:
folic acid and flavonoids in significant quantity

Spinach:
very rich in folic acid, vitamin C and carotene

Fennel:
rich in folic acid; very rich in vitamin C and carotene

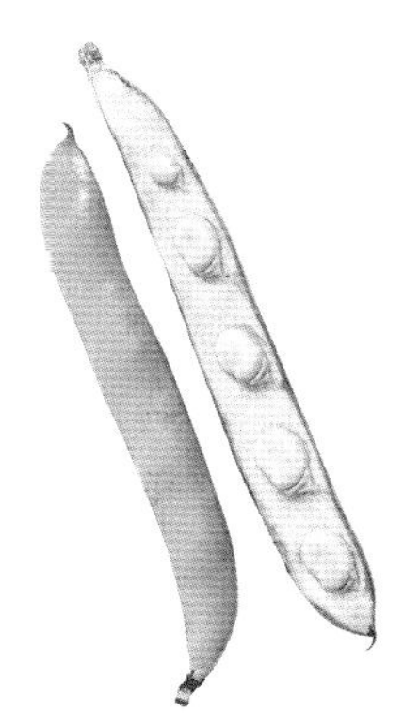

Broad beans:
rich in vitamin C

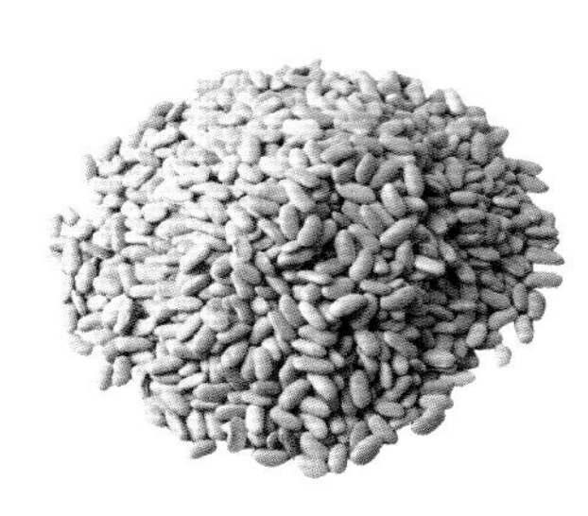

Beans (white or red):
folic acid in significant quantity

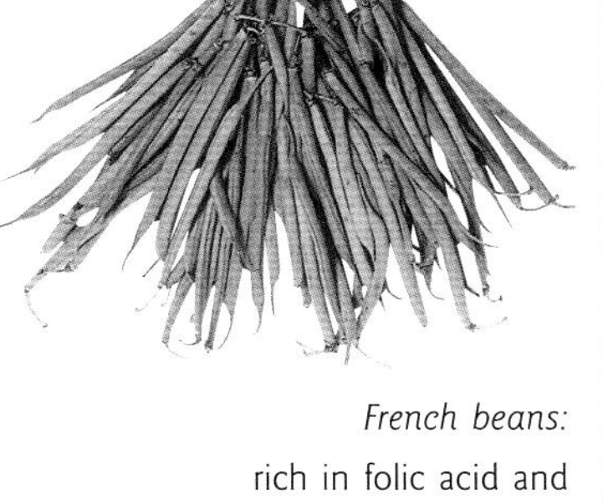

French beans:
rich in folic acid and vitamin C; flavonoids in significant quantity

Lettuce and other salad leaves:
rich in folic acid and flavonoids; vitamin C in significant quantity

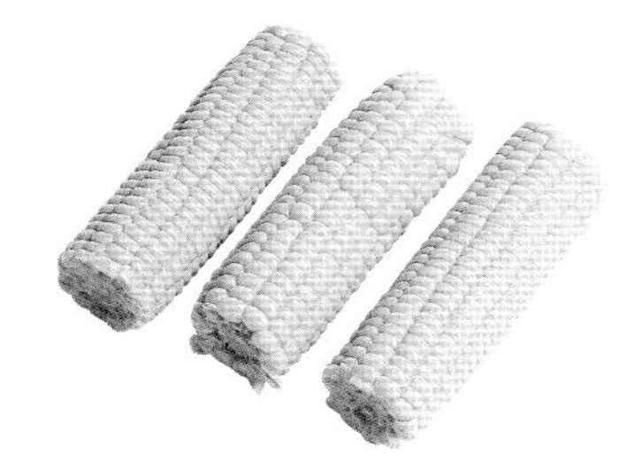

Sweetcorn:
folic acid and vitamin C in significant quantity

Turnips:
rich in vitamin C

Onions:
rich in flavonoids

Sorrel:
very rich in folic acid, vitamin C and carotene

Rich protective elements of vegetables for health

Squash and melons:
rich in vitamin C

Parsley:
very rich in folic acid, vitamin C and carotene; rich in flavonoids

Peas:
folic acid and vitamin C in significant quantity

Dandelion leaves:
very rich in folic acid and carotene; rich in vitamin C

Leeks:
rich in folic acid, vitamin C and carotene; flavonoids in significant quantity

Peppers:
very rich in vitamin C; carotene in significant quantity

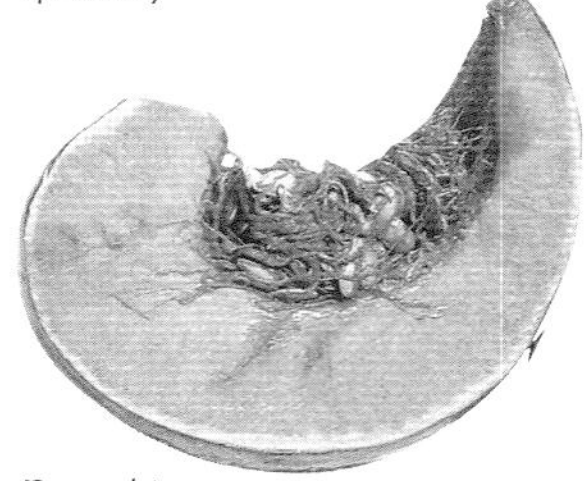

Pumpkins:
rich in carotene

Purslane:
rich in vitamin C; carotene in significant quantity

Radishes:
folic acid in significant quantity; rich in vitamin C

Swede:
rich in vitamin C; carotene in significant quantity

Tomatoes:
rich in vitamin C; carotene in significant quantity

Preserving the vitamins and minerals found in foods

Some methods of preparing ingredients preserve vitamins and protective elements better than others. Here is a brief summary of how to prepare foods in order to make the most of their health benefits.

- Consume fresh foods within 48 hours after their purchase.
- Protect them from heat, light, humidity and air. Place vegetables in a cellar or in the salad drawer of the refrigerator.
- Do not leave vegetables soaking in water. Wash them quickly under running water.
- Limit the amount of water used for boiling and the cooking time.
- Do not store the food for a long time after cooking. Eat, if possible, the skins of fruits and vegetables, but make sure that you wash them thoroughly first.

Cereals, bread, pulses and grains

bulgar wheat

broad beans

white and red beans

Cretan bread

potatoes

pasta

At each meal, you can eat freely from a choice of bread, dried pulses and cereal-based foods, as they provide the vegetable proteins and the essential slow-release carbohydrate indispensable for the muscles, internal organs and brain. In addition, dried pulses, bread, brown rice, bulgar wheat and oat flakes are rich in protective nutrients, such as magnesium and folic acid.

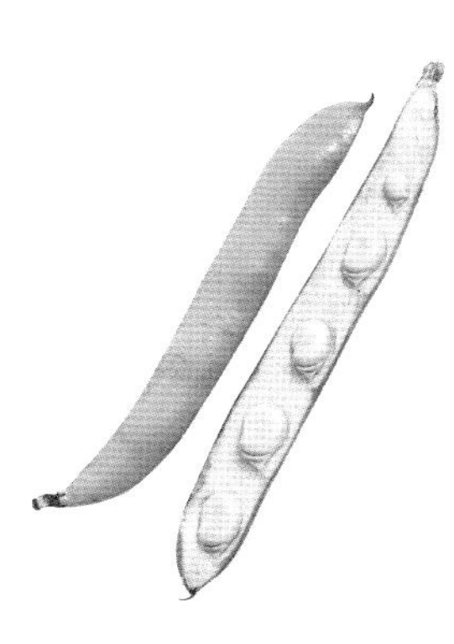

This food group includes:

- Cereals or foods of cereal origin: rice, semolina, wheat, pasta, flours and bread
- Dried pulses: lentils, chickpeas, split peas, kidney beans, haricot beans, brown beans, flageolet beans and broad beans
- Soya beans
- Potatoes and cassava (in the form of tapioca).

Among the starches are the dried pulses and wholegrain cereals – brown rice, wholemeal bread, rye bread – that are thought to help prevent certain types of cancer. Dried pulses are an important source of folic acid and polyphenols, as are the green peas and beans that fight the proliferation of cancerous cells. Dried pulses and foods of cereal origin are equally beneficial in helping to protect against cardiovascular problems and diabetes, thanks to their abundance of folic acid, but equally thanks to their wealth in fibre and the presence of vegetable proteins.

Eat cereals and pulses together. Do not use them separately, as they are complementary. Serve them together with the main dish. When you are not serving a mixture of grains and pulses, serve wholegrain bread instead.

Fish: a favourite

- Traditionally, Cretans eat fish four times a week, notably sardines and mackerel, oily fish which contain omega-3 fatty acids.
- Omega-3 fatty acids diminish the build-up of triglycerides (harmful fats) in the heart as well as the formation of plaque in the arteries.
- Omega-3 fatty acids inhibit the spread of cancerous cells, as demonstrated in some experimental studies. This finding has been corroborated by the results found among a very different group of people. Inuit, big eaters of oily, cold sea fish, herring and salmon, which are also rich in omega-3, benefit in the same way from its cardiovascular protection.
- For your health – and also for your pleasure – you should eat fish regularly, especially the oily varieties which are rich in omega-3.

Oily Fish

RECOMMENDED FOR EVERYBODY	NOT RECOMMENDED FOR PEOPLE WITH EXCESS WEIGHT
Eel	
Fresh anchovies or canned in brine	Anchovies canned in oil
Halibut	Fish canned in oil
Herring, fresh or smoked, or pickled in vinegar	
Mackerel, fresh or smoked, or pickled in white wine	
Dogfish or shark	
Fresh sardines	Sardines canned in oil
Fresh or smoked salmon	
Tuna, fresh or canned in brine	Tuna canned in oil
Trout	
Fish eggs, caviar	
	Fried fish or fish coated with breadcrumbs or prepared as fishcakes

Meat, poultry and eggs: preparation

Diets rich in meat are especially harmful, particularly if they are also low in the consumption of fruit and vegetables. Do not feel obliged to limit yourself, as Cretans do, to two or three meat or poultry dishes a week, but limit the quantities. About 100 g (3½ oz) is a large portion. Do not forget to eat a large quantity of starches and vegetables.

Choose meats or poultry with little fat. However, although lamb is fatty, it differs from other meats because it is beneficial, even in modest quantities, in providing omega-3 fatty acids, which are helpful for the heart and the arteries.

Limit yourself to four eggs a week, including those used in sauces and desserts, if you have cardiovascular problems, high blood cholesterol levels, diabetes or arterial hypertension – or if you smoke.

Less fatty meats and more fatty meats

	PARTS WITH LITTLE FAT	PARTS WITH MORE FAT
Offal	Heart, liver, kidneys	Ox tongue, brains
Lamb		Cutlets, leg, shoulder
Beef	Steak, roast, minced with less than 5 per cent fat	Rib, stewing meat, minced with more than 15 per cent or 20 per cent fat
Cold meats	Ham cooked without fat, lean back bacon	Sausages, black pudding, haggis, salami and garlic sausage, raw ham
New meats	Alligator, ostrich, emu	Buffalo
Game	Boar, venison	
Rabbit	All pieces	
Pork	Fillet without fat	Chops, leg, shoulder, spare ribs, loin
Veal	Cutlets, escalope, fillet	Leg, best end of neck
Poultry and feathered game	Turkey, chicken, poussin, quail	Duck, pheasant, goose, pigeon

Milk products: yogurt and cheese

To follow the Cretan regime, give up or at least cut down on full-cream milk, double cream and full-fat cheeses and, instead, eat fresh cheeses and fermented dairy products, like yogurt, all rich in calcium. A piece of low-fat cheese and one or two servings of yogurt a day constitute a good amount.

Wine: in reasonable quantity

Presented as the banner of the Cretan diet, red wine has, of course, some advantages, but is not essential. In fact, you can also find most of the protective nutrients found in wine in fruit and vegetables, without worrying about any adverse effects associated with alcohol.

The daily intake of two or three glasses of wine is associated with a reduced rate of death from such cardiovascular problems as heart attacks, hardening of the arteries and strokes by about 35 per cent. This same daily intake of wine is also credited with a reduction of the risk of many cancers by 20 per cent. These benefits are primarily for men; as one glass of alcohol a day increases the risk of breast cancer in women by 9 per cent and three glasses by 41 per cent. Finally, the moderate consumption of wine is associated with a reduction of Alzheimer's disease, dementia and senility, according to research conducted at the University of Bordeaux. Other scientific research will have to confirm these results before red wine can actually be considered a preventative factor in the intellectual alterations of old age.

Regularly drinking red wine can, therefore, have a beneficial effect on health as long as it does not exceed the 'recommended dose' – two daily glasses for women, three for men. Over those limits, the effects of alcohol reverse themselves, and the risk of harm to the heart and arteries – arterial hypertension and cardiac weakness – cancer, notably cancer of the throat and liver, and the brain – nervous conditions, and insanity rapidly increase.

If you don't enjoy wine, don't force yourself to drink it! In fact, it is not the red wine, but the combination of foods, as well as the convivial manner in which the Cretans eat them, that results in the benefits of the Cretan system.

If you regularly drink wine without exceeding two glasses a day for a woman – 250 ml (8 fl oz) – or three glasses a day for a man – half a 750 ml (1¼ pint) bottle – carry on. If you drink more, reduce the quantity; otherwise, you risk weakening your health from the harmful effects of alcohol.

Finally, do not forget to place two glasses at each table setting, one for water to refresh, the other for wine to enjoy in small doses.

Vices and virtues

The health benefits of regular and moderate consumption of red wine are quickly reversed by excessive consumption of wine or any other alcoholic drink.

For example, the heavy consumption of alcohol in France is the root cause of many medical, psychological, and socio-familial difficulties in a country with 59 million people. It is also responsible for 40,000 deaths, for one-third of the road accidents, for 80 per cent of scuffles, brawls, and domestic violence, and for 15 per cent of work-related accidents.

CRETE

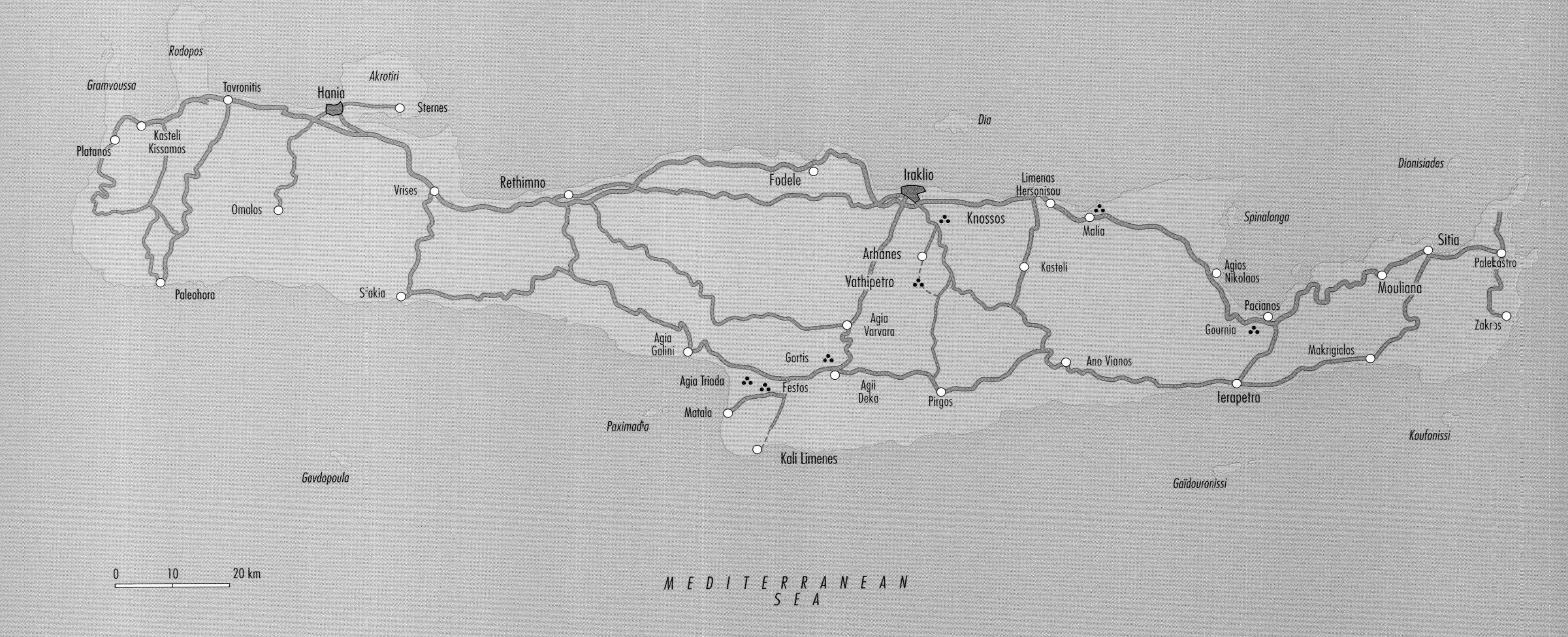

The island of Crete, known and visited for its antiquities, is also an agricultural land. Tomatoes, cucumbers and bananas are cultivated in Lerapetra, while Hania and Fodele are known for their citrus fruits. Vineyards can be found all around Arhanes, Peza, Mouliana, Kali Limenes, Knossos and Vathipetro.

Some villages have feasts centred around their harvests – chestnuts in Hania, wine in Rethimno, Hania and Iraklio, raisins in Sitia, where the harvest is celebrated every year from August 19 to the 22.

Olive oil: a must

Fat comes primarily from oils, cream, butter, margarine and mayonnaise and may be of animal or vegetable origin.

Cretans use olive oil, as do people in the rest of the Mediterranean basin, but the ingredients that they cook are naturally not very high in fat. Nutritionists in Britain recommend a moderate amount of fat, whether in cooking or on the table – 33 g (1⅔ oz) a day compared with 95 g (3⅓ oz) a day consumed by Cretans. On the other hand, the British diet features naturally fatty foods, such as red meat, full-fat milk and chips, or processed foods, such as crisps, biscuits, sausages, hamburgers, desserts, ice creams and chocolate bars. The quality of the lipids – insoluble fats – varies, therefore, from one dietary system to the other, implying a comparable but rather favourable effect for the Cretan system, thanks to the olive oil, and a rather harmful effect for the British system.

Choosing the oil

If you like oils that have little taste, choose rapeseed oil or, for cooking, groundnut oil. If you prefer olive oil, stronger in flavour and rich in flavonoids, do not hesitate to mix it with rapeseed oil (for its omega-3) in your salad dressings. Together, they will provide monounsaturated fatty acids in optimal quantities. Walnut oil, rich in omega-3 and flavour, is a good alternative.

The fatty acids

Fat is made up of basic units called fatty acids. There are four groups – saturated, monounsaturated, omega-6 and omega-3. Monounsaturated fatty acids should form the greatest portion of the diet, as was the case during the past centuries, while the fatty saturated acids should not exceed a 25 per cent total. The proportion between the quantities of omega-6 fatty acids and omega-3 fatty acids should be close to 5; but today it is over 10.

The Cretan diet approaches the optimum equilibrium: a lot of monounsaturated fatty acids (in olive oil), a reasonable quantity of omega-6 fatty acids (in small quantity in olive oil) and of saturated fat (meat and dairy products) and omega-3 fatty acids, which Cretans find in purslane, octopus, fish, snails, walnuts and almonds.

If you want to achieve this optimal equilibrium for yourself, you must use olive oil, groundnut oil or rapeseed oil. All three are rich in monounsaturated fatty acids, are low in saturated fats and contain omega-6 fatty acids in reasonable quantity – neither too much nor too little for your diet. But where do you find omega-3? You can do as the Cretans do – eat purslane, octopus, oily fish such as mackerel, sardines, herring, tuna and salmon, snails and desserts made with walnuts and almonds or other nuts. You can choose oils rich in omega-3 fatty acids – nut oils, soya and rapeseed oil. Use them in salad dressings or for cooking on a low heat, but do not use them for deep-frying.

Other oils commonly used in western Europe are low in omega-3, even the olive oil. Rapeseed oil is more interesting, as it is the only one high in monounsaturated fatty acids and in omega-3 fatty acids at the same time.

Combining health and simplicity with pleasure and conviviality

Cretan cuisine is traditionally savoury and very colourful. The texture of food is characteristically crisp – raw or lightly cooked vegetables – or firm – starches cooked *al dente* or bread. Cretans do not balk at chewing their food. The flavours are varied, often sharp or acidic – garlic, lemon, vinegar, onions, spices and aromatic herbs.

Cretan cooking is neither bland nor vegetarian. Even if it gives a major role to foods of vegetable origin, such as fruit, starches, bread and, certainly, olive oil, it also includes meat, fish, cheeses and yogurts and desserts. The preparation is usually simple; it is the choice of foods, the quality of the ingredients and their combination that brings out the savoury flavours rather than the style of cooking or laboriously made sauces.

Cretan cooking is to be enjoyed and shared with friends or family. Adapt these principles to suit your tastes and the tastes of your family and friends in order to succeed in creating simple and savoury dishes for everyday meals and for festive occasions. The recipes that follow have only one purpose – to help you. And, like the Cretans themselves, do not hesitate to adopt a certain ritual in the order of dishes you serve. From the moment you feel ready to accept the pleasures of the Cretan way of life and way of eating, your whole family will accept the rules that you have chosen. In fact, taking pleasure in the food and enjoying the company are essential for the child who is learning to eat with the grown ups.

Finally, do not feel that you have to follow our advice to the letter. Do not hesitate to eat dishes from a different cuisine two or three times a week or go to a restaurant with friends. It is long-term balance that counts and that will not be altered with an occasional unbalanced meal.

Traditional Cretan cooking has proved its advantages for general health. Even if we generally eat in a healthy manner, Cretan cooking can improve our shape, wellbeing and health.

recipes

aubergines with a spoon

SERVES 6
6 tomatoes
6 aubergines
3 tablespoons olive oil
2 onions, chopped
4 parsley sprigs, chopped
4 basil sprigs, chopped
250 g (8 oz) feta or pecorino cheese, diced
salt and pepper

Preparation: *40 minutes* • **cooking:** *40 minutes*

Place the tomatoes in a bowl and pour over boiling water to cover. Leave for 1–2 minutes, then drain, cut a cross in the stem end of each tomato, and peel off the skins. Cut in half and squeeze gently to remove any excess water and the seeds. Dice the flesh.

Cut off the top third of each aubergine and carefully scoop out the flesh. Sprinkle the shells with salt and set aside.

Heat 2 tablespoons of the oil in a frying pan and fry the onions until golden brown. Add the aubergine flesh, then the diced tomatoes and chopped parsley. Season with salt and pepper to taste. Cover and cook over a very low heat for 5 minutes. Remove the lid and cook for a further 5 minutes to allow the excess liquid to evaporate.

Transfer the mixture to a bowl and mash coarsely with a wooden spatula. Stir in the basil. Taste and adjust the seasoning and set aside to cool.

Pat the aubergine shells dry with kitchen paper. Add the diced cheese to the filling. Brush the base of an ovenproof dish that will hold the aubergines in a single layer with the remaining oil. Spoon the filling into the aubergine shells and arrange them in the dish. Bake in a preheated oven, 180°C (350°F), Gas Mark 4, for 30 minutes.

Place a filled aubergine on each plate and carry them to the dining table. They will have cooled slightly by the time your guests are seated. That is how they are supposed to be enjoyed.

Basil enhances flavour. In Greek, basilikos *means 'royal'. The herb is said to have tranquillizing virtues. Once dried, it loses its aroma, so it is better to eat it fresh. Disdained for a long time, the aubergine, called 'the apple of fools', first appeared on dining tables in the nineteenth century.*

Aubergine salad with sesame seeds

Serves 6

3 large, ripe tomatoes
6 tablespoons olive oil
2 small onions, finely chopped
1 teaspoon sesame seeds
50 g (2 oz) raisins
3 aubergines, sliced
6 parsley sprigs, chopped
salt and pepper

Prepare 1 day ahead • preparation and cooking: *30 minutes*

Place the tomatoes in a bowl and pour over boiling water to cover. Leave for 1–2 minutes, then drain, cut a cross in the stem end of each tomato, and peel off the skins. Deseed and cut the flesh into large pieces.

Heat 2 tablespoons of the olive oil in a saucepan and fry the onions over a low heat, stirring occasionally, for 5 minutes, until golden brown. Add the tomatoes, sesame seeds and raisins and season to taste with salt and pepper. Simmer, uncovered for 5 minutes to allow the liquid to evaporate.

Heat the remaining olive oil in a nonstick frying pan. Add the aubergines, in batches if necessary, and cook over a low heat for 5 minutes. Season to taste with salt and pepper, then turn the slices over, cover the pan and cook for a further 5 minutes. Remove from the pan with a slotted spoon and drain on kitchen paper.

Arrange the aubergine slices in a serving dish, spoon over the onion and tomato sauce and set aside to cool to room temperature. Sprinkle with chopped parsley before serving.

In ancient Greece, sesame seeds were considered good for health. Today, Cretans continue the tradition by sprinkling their cakes with sesame seeds.

Squid and artichoke salad

Serves 6
6 large globe artichokes
500 g (1 lb) prepared squid
6 tablespoons olive oil
2 garlic cloves, chopped
1 small bunch of parsley, chopped
4 tablespoons lemon juice
salt and pepper

Preparation: *15 minutes* • **cooking:** *10 minutes*

Cut or break off the artichoke stems, remove the outer leaves and the central choke. Rinse the artichokes under cold running water. Cook in a large saucepan of boiling water for 30–40 minutes.

Check the artichokes as they cook. When ready, the leaves should pull off easily but the bases should remain firm. Drain well, then pull off the leaves and reserve both the leaves and hearts.

Cut the squid into small squares. Heat 1 tablespoon of the olive oil in a frying pan. Season the squid pieces to taste with salt and pepper and fry, stirring frequently, for 5 minutes. Remove with a slotted spoon and drain in a colander. Transfer to a bowl, sprinkle with the garlic and parsley and drizzle with a little of the remaining olive oil and some of the lemon juice.

Prepare a dressing by mixing the remaining olive oil and lemon juice, then season to taste with salt and pepper. Carefully mix the artichoke hearts with the squid, pour over the dressing and toss gently. Serve on individual plates, surrounded with some artichoke leaves.

The squid has ten tentacles, two of them longer than the others, and a beak that allows it to eat shellfish. The smaller it is, the better it tastes. In Crete, this dish would probably be prepared with octopus, which you can substitute if you like, providing you can find prepared and tenderized octopus.

cucumber mint soup

Serves 6

3 cucumbers,
250 g (8 oz) feta cheese
1 small bunch of mint, leaves cut into thin strips
4 tablespoons lemon juice
2 tablespoons olive oil
pinch of freshly grated nutmeg
1 teaspoon salt
pepper

Preparation: *15 minutes* • **cooking:** *none*

Peel and grate the cucumbers into a serving bowl. Reserve a little feta for the garnish and crumble the remainder into the bowl. Add the mint leaves, lemon juice, olive oil and nutmeg and season with salt and pepper to taste. Toss well to mix. Crumble over the remaining feta and serve immediately.

In the seventeenth century, physicians recommended pickling cucumber in vinegar to make it more digestible. Today some cooks steam it for 1 minute before serving it in a salad. Lemon juice replaces vinegar in this recipe.

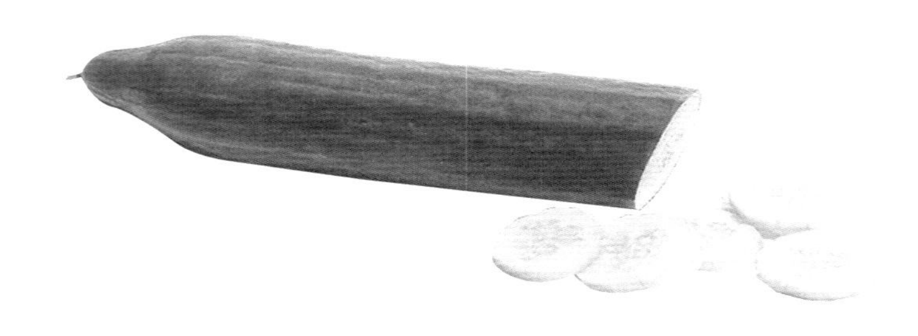

'Mille-feuille' of aubergine with crab

Serves 6

4 large, ripe tomatoes
1 garlic clove, halved
125 ml (4 fl oz) olive oil
pinch of sugar
3 basil sprigs, leaves coarsely torn
2 aubergines, thinly sliced lengthways
500 g (1 lb) fresh or frozen crab meat
salt and pepper
6 basil leaves, to garnish

Preparation: *30 minutes* • **Preparation of tomatoes:** *1 hour*
cooking: *10 minutes*

Place the tomatoes in a bowl and pour over boiling water to cover. Leave for 1–2 minutes, then drain, cut a cross in the stem end of each tomato, and peel off the skins. Cut in half, deseed and place in a colander. Sprinkle with salt and set aside for 1 hour to drain.

Transfer the tomatoes to a bowl. Add the garlic, 1 tablespoon of the olive oil and the sugar and season to taste with pepper. Add the torn basil leaves, stir well and set aside.

Heat the remaining oil in a frying pan and cook the aubergines, a few slices at a time, for 5 minutes on each side. Season to taste with salt and pepper. Remove from the pan with a slotted spoon and drain on kitchen paper. Keep warm while you are cooking the remaining batches.

Drain the crab meat, if necessary, and divide it into 6 portions. Layer the aubergine slices on top of each other like a mille-feuille, covering each slice with crab meat. Serve warm with tomato sauce and garnished with a basil leaf.

The tomato, which is native to South America, took a long time to become popular in Europe because it belongs to the solanaceous family and was considered, like its relative deadly nightshade, to be a poisonous plant.

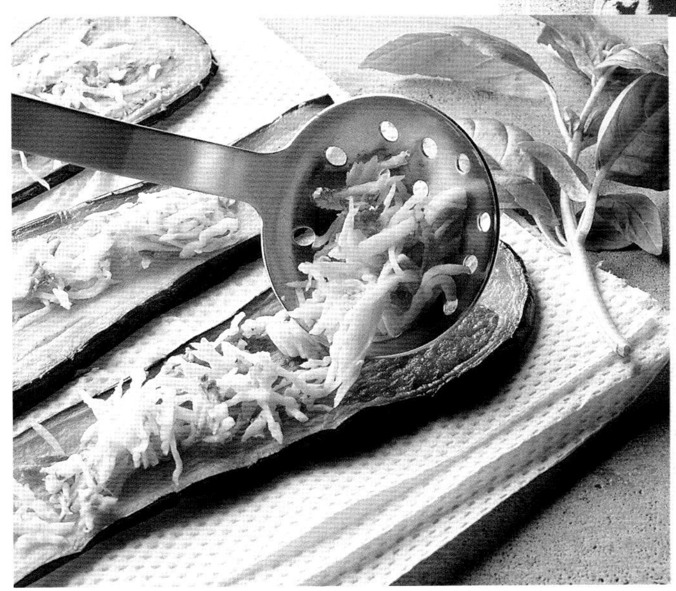

stuffed courgette flowers

SERVES 4
2 tomatoes
125 ml (4 fl oz) olive oil
1 onion, chopped
4 mint sprigs, finely chopped
4 dill sprigs, finely chopped
6 parsley sprigs, finely chopped
4 tablespoons lemon juice
50 g (2 oz) cooked rice
1 teaspoon dried mint
20 courgette flowers (see note below recipe)
salt and pepper

Preparation: *30 minutes* • **cooking**: *20 minutes*

Place the tomatoes in a bowl and pour over boiling water to cover. Leave for 1–2 minutes, then drain, cut a cross in the stem end of each tomato, and peel off the skins. Halve, deseed and coarsely chop the flesh.

Heat the olive oil in a frying pan and fry the onion over a low heat, stirring occasionally, for 5 minutes, until softened. Add the fresh herbs, lemon juice and tomatoes and stir. Add the rice and dried mint and season to taste with salt and pepper. Cook, stirring, for a few seconds until the stuffing is dry, then remove the pan from the heat.

Spoon the stuffing into the courgette flowers and fold the petals over. Place them close together in another frying pan. Pour a little water into the base of the pan; cover and simmer for 20 minutes. Add more water, as required. Taste and adjust the seasoning, if necessary, before serving.

In the summer, courgettes are sometimes sold with their flowers attached. You are most likely to find these in vegetable markets. They are too perishable for the long transportation times of most supermarkets. If you grow your own courgettes, you can use the flowers for this recipe. If you cannot find flowers - and you could substitute hollyhocks if you grow these - use 8–10 lettuce leaves, blanched in boiling water for 1 minute and drained, instead.

figs with feta stuffing

SERVES 6

18 large, ripe fresh figs
100 g (3½ oz) feta cheese, diced
2 tablespoons olive oil
salt and pepper
fresh fig leaves, to garnish (optional)

Preparation: *10 minutes* • **cooking:** *2 minutes*

Cut off and reserve the tops of the figs to make 'lids'. Gently push a cube of feta into each fig and season lightly with salt and pepper, bearing in mind that feta is already quite salty. Replace the 'lids'.

Lightly brush olive oil over an oval, ovenproof platter. Arrange the stuffed figs on the platter and gently brush them with oil.

Cook under a preheated grill for 2 minutes, until the cheese has melted and the figs are lightly golden.

Garnish individual plates with fig leaves and carefully place 3 figs on each plate. Serve immediately.

The nutritive value of figs has been recognized since ancient times. Rufus, a doctor in the first century BC, recommended figs to young girls. When they are dried, figs are a more concentrated source of energy and so are recommended for athletes. In the Middle Ages, they featured in Lenten menus, either roasted or fresh for dessert.

warm tomatoes with goat's cheese

Serves 6

12 small, ripe tomatoes
6 Rocamadour or other small goat's cheeses
2–3 savory sprigs, chopped
1 egg, beaten
salt and pepper

Preparation: *15 minutes* • **preparation of tomatoes:** *1 hour*
cooking: *10 minutes*

Slice off the tops of the tomatoes. With a teaspoon, carefully scoop out the pulp and seeds without piercing the shells. Reserve the pulp and discard the seeds. Sprinkle the insides of the tomatoes with a pinch of salt and place them on a platter. Set aside for at least 1 hour.

Place the cheeses, tomato pulp and savory in a bowl and mash with a fork. Season to taste with salt and pepper. Mix in the egg to make a thick paste.

Spoon the cheese filling into the tomato shells. Arrange them in a single layer on an ovenproof plate and bake in a preheated oven, 160°C (325°F), Gas Mark 3, for 10 minutes. Turn off the heat but leave the tomatoes to cool in the oven for several minutes before serving.

Goat's cheese has been known since ancient times. In the eleventh book of the Iliad, *Hecamede prepares a drink to quench the thirst of Nestor and Machaon. While the heroes are resting in their beds, she mixes the goat's cheese in the wine of Praminos and sprinkles the liquid with flour.*

Marinated fish

Serves 6–8

1 teaspoon chopped fresh dill
6 tablespoons olive oil
4 teaspoons coarse salt
1 tablespoon crushed peppercorns
1 tablespoon sugar
2 sea bass fillets, skinned, weighing about 500 g (1 lb) in total
toasted bread, to serve

Preparation: *10 minutes* • **cooking:** *none*
marinating: *48 hours*

Start preparing the fish 2 days before you intend to serve it. Mix together the dill, olive oil, coarse salt, crushed peppercorns and sugar in a bowl or jug.

Pour a third of the marinade into a dish. Add a fish fillet, cover with half of the remaining mixture, add the second fish fillet and pour over the remaining marinade. Cover with foil, place a weight on top and set aside in the refrigerator to marinate for 2 days.

Remove the fish fillets from the marinade and drain well, reserving the marinade. Place the fillets on a chopping board and slice thinly. Arrange overlapping slices in 2 rows on a serving platter or individual plates and spoon over a little of the reserved marinade. Serve with toasted bread.

The Romans identified two kinds of peppercorns – the long one, gathered ripe and dried in the sun, and the white one, gathered green. We make the distinction between black pepper, which is dried before maturity, and sweeter white pepper. If you mix white and black peppercorns in a pepper mill and add coriander seeds and dried chillies, you will bring a Cretan touch to your seasoning.

bulgar wheat with coriander and olives

Serves 6

250 g (8 oz) fine bulgar wheat
1 small bunch of flat leaf parsley, chopped
12 black olives, pitted and chopped
65 g (2½ oz) raisins
4 tablespoons lemon juice
2 tablespoons olive oil
1 teaspoon ground cinnamon
1 teaspoon ground coriander
salt and pepper

Preparation: *10 minutes* • **soaking:** *1 hour*
cooking: *none* • **chilling:** *1 hour*

Place the bulgar wheat in a bowl, add cold water to cover and set aside to soak for 1 hour.

Drain the bulgar wheat and place in a serving bowl. Add the parsley, olives and raisins.

Mix together the lemon juice and olive oil in a jug, pour the dressing over the bulgar wheat mixture and mix well. Add the cinnamon and coriander and season to taste with salt and pepper. Mix well again, then set aside for 1 hour for the flavours to infuse.

Taste and adjust the seasoning, if necessary, before serving.

Bulgar wheat is becoming an increasingly popular cereal, perhaps as a result of the proliferation of Greek Cypriot supermarkets and Greek restaurants. As well as making delicious salads, as here, it is a classic complement to lamb (see opposite and recipe on page 104).

Mussels with julienne vegetables and saffron

Serves 6

3-4 tarragon stalks
2 kg (4 lb) fresh mussels
2 shallots, finely chopped
125 ml (4 fl oz) dry white wine
1 tablespoon olive oil
12 saffron threads
1 leek, white part only cut into julienne strips
2 carrots, cut into julienne strips
2 celery sticks, cut into julienne strips
salt and pepper

Preparation and cooking: *30 minutes*

Remove the leaves from the tarragon stalks and reserve the stalks. Scrub the mussels under cold running water and pull off the beards. Discard any with damaged shells or that do not shut immediately when sharply tapped.

Place half the shallots in a large saucepan with the wine and bring to the boil. Add the mussels, cover and cook over a high heat, shaking the pan occasionally, until they have opened. Transfer the mussels to a bowl using a slotted spoon and discard any that remain shut. Strain the cooking liquid through a sieve lined with muslin and reserve. Remove the mussels from their shells.

Heat the oil in a frying pan and cook the remaining shallot, the tarragon stems and saffron until the shallot is softened and translucent. Add the leek, carrots and celery, season to taste with salt and pepper and simmer for 4 minutes, until tender. Remove from the heat, add the mussels, sprinkle with tarragon leaves and serve warm.

Saffron, consisting of the dried stigmas of the Crocus sativus, *is the world's most expensive spice. It has an incomparable flavour and there is no satisfactory substitute.*

Mussel pilaf

SERVES 6

2 kg (4 lb) fresh mussels
500 g (1 lb) tomatoes
100 ml (3½ fl oz) olive oil
2 small onions, chopped
200 g (7 oz) rice, rinsed and drained
coarse sea salt and pepper

Preparation: *45 minutes* • **cooking:** *30 minutes*

Scrub the mussels under cold running water and pull off the beards. Discard any with damaged shells or that do not shut immediately when sharply tapped with the back of a knife.

Place the mussels in a large, heavy-based saucepan and add 150 ml (¼ pint) water, cover tightly and bring to the boil over a high heat. Cook, shaking the pan frequently, for 4–5 minutes, until all the mussels have opened. Drain well, reserving the cooking liquid. Remove the mussels from their shells discarding any that have remained shut. Strain the reserved cooking liquid through a sieve lined with muslin into a measuring jug and make up to 500 ml (17 fl oz) with water.

Place the tomatoes in a bowl and pour over boiling water to cover. Leave for 1–2 minutes, then drain, cut a cross in the stem end of each tomato, and peel off the skins. Chop the flesh.

Heat the olive oil in another saucepan. Cook the onions over a medium heat, stirring occasionally, for about 8 minutes, until golden brown. Add the tomatoes and season with sea salt and pepper.

Add the rice and stir well. Pour in the reserved mussel cooking liquid mixture and season with salt and pepper to taste.

Add the mussels to the saucepan and simmer over a low heat for 15–20 minutes, until the the rice is tender.

Serve the pilaf immediately

In Crete, this pilaf would be prepared with fresh snails. If you want to try this, you can substitute thawed frozen or drained canned snails for the mussels adding them with the rice. Add 500ml (17 fl oz) water instead of the reserved cooking liquid mixture.

Spinach Salad with Broad Beans

Serves 6

6 baby globe artichokes
125 ml (4 fl oz) lemon juice
6 tablespoons olive oil
1 teaspoon cumin seeds
250 g (8 oz) baby spinach leaves
375 g (12 oz) shelled baby broad beans
375 g (12 oz) shelled petits pois
100 g (3½ oz) pecorino cheese
salt and pepper

Preparation: *40 minutes* • **cooking**: *none*

Break off the stems of the artichokes, cut the leaves two-thirds from the top, remove the central chokes and rub a little lemon juice on the cut surfaces. Cut the artichokes in half and then slice thinly.

To make the dressing, whisk together the olive oil, remaining lemon juice and the cumin in a salad bowl and season to taste with salt and pepper. Add the spinach, artichokes, beans and peas and toss lightly.

Divide the salad into 6 portions and arrange on individual plates. Using a vegetable peeler, shave the pecorino into fine strips over the salads.

At the time of the Roman Empire, artichokes were recommended for the elderly, apathetic, or melancholic. In the seventeenth century, they were considered an aphrodisiac. Young ladies were forbidden to eat them.

citrus monkfish salad

Serves 6

2 red peppers
4 tablespoons olive oil
3 lemons
2 green apples, such as Granny Smiths, peeled, cored and sliced
2 oranges, peeled and cut into segments
300 g (10 oz) smoked monkfish fillet
250 g (8 oz) mixed salad leaves
1 tablespoon balsamic vinegar
2–3 flat leaf parsley sprigs, chopped
salt and pepper

Preparation: *25 minutes* • **cooking:** *20 minutes*
marinating: *1 hour*

On the day before you plan to serve, place the peppers on a baking sheet and cook under a preheated grill, turning frequently, until the skins are blackened and charred. Using tongs, transfer to a plastic bag and tie the top. When the peppers are cool enough to handle, rub off the skins, then halve and deseed them. Cut the flesh into fine strips and place in a bowl. Sprinkle them with 1 tablespoon of the olive oil, season to taste with salt and pepper, cover and set aside.

On the same day, peel 2 of the lemons and cut them into wedges. Heat 1 tablespoon of the remaining olive oil in a saucepan. Add the apples, oranges and lemon wedges, season with salt and pepper and cook for 5 minutes. Remove from the heat and set aside.

The next day, remove any remaining membrane from the fish and squeeze the remaining lemon. About 1 hour before serving, slice the fish thinly, place in a glass or china dish and sprinkle with the lemon juice. Cover and set aside in a cool place to marinate.

Place the salad leaves in a bowl and sprinkle with the remaining olive oil and the vinegar and season to taste with salt and pepper. Toss well, then arrange on individual plates with the fish in the middle, the peppers on one side and the fruits on the other side. Sprinkle with the parsley and serve.

Smoked monkfish is not a Cretan speciality, but it is excellent served without further cooking. You could also use smoked mackerel or very fresh smoked haddock.

scallops in fresh tomato sauce

Serves 6

500 g (1 lb) tomatoes
6 tablespoons olive oil
1 bunch of dill, finely chopped
12 parsley sprigs, finely chopped
6 mint sprigs, finely chopped
1 garlic clove, peeled, but left whole
1 tablespoon coarse sea salt
24 large scallops, shelled
salt and pepper

Preparation: *15 minutes* • **cooking:** *25 minutes*

Place the tomatoes in a bowl and pour over boiling water to cover. Leave for 1–2 minutes, then drain, cut a cross in the stem end of each tomato, and peel off the skins. Chop the flesh and place in a bowl.

Heat 4 tablespoons of the olive oil in a saucepan. Add the tomatoes and stir for several seconds, then add the herbs and garlic and season with salt and pepper to taste. Half-cover the pan, lower the heat and simmer for 20 minutes.

Heat the remaining olive oil with the sea salt in a nonstick saucepan. Add the scallops and cook for 2 minutes on each side, until they turn a golden colour. Remove from the pan immediately.

To serve, divide the scallops among individual serving plates and spoon over the tomato sauce, discarding the garlic.

Be careful not to overcook the scallops or they will toughen. If you are buying shelled scallops, ask if they are fresh or frozen. Fresh scallops are slightly translucent, while frozen ones tend to be an opaque milky white. Fresh scallops have a better texture and flavour than frozen.

prawns with cucumber

SERVES 4

1 cucumber, peeled and thinly sliced
2 tablespoons wine vinegar
pinch of sugar
16 raw Mediterranean or other large prawns, peeled and deveined
2 tablespoons olive oil
10 saffron threads
pinch of dried red chilli
1 tablespoon coriander seeds
coarse sea salt and pepper
4 coriander sprigs, chopped, to garnish

Preparation and cooking: *30 minutes*
marinating: *12 hours*

The day before you intend to serve, place the cucumber slices in a bowl and cover with cold water. Stir in the wine vinegar, 1 teaspoon salt and the sugar. Set aside to marinate for 12 hours.

On the same day, place the prawns in a dish, drizzle with a little olive oil and sprinkle with saffron and crushed red chilli. Season with pepper.

The next day, drain the cucumber. Arrange the slices, overlapping slightly, in a circle on individual plates and sprinkle with coriander seeds.

Heat the remaining oil in a frying pan and cook the prawns over a high heat for 1–2 minutes on each side. Season with sea salt. Spoon the prawns into the centres of the plates. Sprinkle with chopped coriander and serve.

If possible, buy fresh rather than cooked prawns. If they are frozen, thaw them thoroughly before cooking. Don't overcook them or they will toughen, but there is no benefit in undercooking, which may even be dangerous. Cook until they have just changed colour. If using cooked prawns, simply heat through briefly before serving.

keftedes

Serves 8

3 large potatoes
1 white onion
500 g (1 lb) minced beef
1 egg
10 parsley sprigs, finely chopped
2 mint sprigs, finely chopped
1 teaspoon dried mint
4 tablespoons fresh white breadcrumbs
125 ml (4 fl oz) olive oil
4 tablespoons lemon juice
1 cos lettuce, cut into thin strips
2-3 spring onions, thinly sliced
salt and pepper
8 coriander sprigs, chopped, to garnish

Preparation: *30 minutes* • **cooking:** *5 minutes*

Grate the potatoes and onion into a sieve, place a weight on top and set aside to drain.

Put the meat in a bowl, make a well in the centre and break the egg into it. Add the fresh herbs and the dried mint and season with salt and pepper.

Dry the potatoes and the onion with a tea towel and add to the meat mixture. Mix by hand to a paste. Add the breadcrumbs, a little at a time, until the mixture is firm, but not dry. Reserve the remaining breadcrumbs on a shallow plate. Shape the meat mixture into small balls by rolling pieces between the palms of your hands. Roll the meatballs in the reserved breadcrumbs to coat evenly.

Make a dressing by mixing 5 tablespoons of the olive oil and the lemon juice in a jug and season to taste with salt and pepper.

Heat the remaining olive oil in a frying pan. Fry the meatballs, in batches if necessary, shaking the pan frequently, for 2 minutes. Remove from the pan with a slotted spoon and drain on kitchen paper.

Toss the lettuce with the spring onions and dressing and arrange on individual plates. Spoon on the meatballs and garnish with the coriander.

In 1593, Admiral Hawkins observed that lemon juice helped treat the men in his company who were afflicted with scurvy. Since then, lemon juice has been used as much in the kitchen as in medicine.

tiropita

Serves 6

3 tablespoons olive oil
2 onions, finely chopped
3 eggs
2 tablespoons chopped dill
250 g (8 oz) feta cheese, crumbled
2 tablespoons milk
24 sheets of filo pastry
125 g (4 oz) butter, melted
salt and pepper

Preparation: *30 minutes* • **cooking**: *40 minutes*

Heat the olive oil in a saucepan and fry the onions over a low heat, stirring occasionally, for 5 minutes.

To prepare the stuffing, beat the eggs with the dill and salt and pepper to taste in a bowl. In another bowl, mash the feta in the milk, then add the mixture to the eggs. Stir in the onions.

Brush a rectangular cake tin with melted butter. Stack 6 sheets of filo in the tin, brushing each with melted butter. Spoon in some of the stuffing, then cover with 6 more sheets of filo, brushing each with melted butter. Cover with more stuffing and continue making layers until all the filo has been used. With your fingers, dampen the top pastry sheet with water.

Bake in a preheated oven, 200°C (400°F), Gas Mark 6, for 40 minutes. Turn off the heat and leave the tin in the oven for 10 more minutes, then serve.

Frozen filo pastry can be bought from Greek delicatessens and most supermarkets. The reason for brushing the sheets with melted butter is to prevent the edges from curling while baking. This allows the sheets of filo pastry to remain crunchy.

terrine of tarama and blinis

SERVES 8–10

200 g (7 oz) white bread, crusts removed
250 ml (8 fl oz) warm milk
1 small onion
200 g (7 oz) smoked cod's roe
1 egg yolk
125 ml (4 fl oz) lemon juice
500 ml (17 fl oz) olive oil
pepper

For the blinis

1½ tablespoons dried yeast
500 ml (17 fl oz) lukewarm milk
2 eggs, separated
pinch of sugar
1 tablespoon olive oil
2 tablespoons semolina
300 g (10 oz) plain flour
salt

Preparation: *30 minutes* • **rising**: *1 hour*
cooking: *10 minutes* • **chilling**: *about 12 hours*

Tear the bread into pieces and place in a bowl. Pour in the milk and set aside to soak. Grate the onion into another bowl. Remove and discard the skin surrounding the roe. Drain the bread and squeeze out any excess liquid.

Mix the roe and bread in a bowl, then add the onion. Add the egg yolk to the lemon juice in a jug and gradually whisk in the the olive oil. Season to taste with pepper. Whisk in 125 ml (4 fl oz) water to stabilize the mixture. Stir the lemon and oil mixture into the cod's roe mixture, spoon into a terrine and chill in the refrigerator overnight.

To prepare the blinis, mix the yeast with a little of the lukewarm milk in a bowl and set aside until frothy. Add the egg yolks, sugar and a pinch of salt to the yeast mixture and mix well. Add 1 teaspoon of the olive oil, drop by drop, and stir it in with a wooden spatula. Add the remaining milk, the semolina and flour, beating well. Set aside for 1 hour.

In a separate bowl, whisk the egg whites until they form soft peaks, then gently fold them into the dough.

Heat a little of the remaining oil in a large, nonstick pan. Add 3 small ladlefuls of the dough and cook for 1 minute on each side.

Keep the blinis warm between two plates on top of a steamer while you finish cooking the rest of the blinis. Serve hot with the terrine of tarama.

Tarama, which is used as the basic ingredient in making taramasalata, can be found in Greek delicatessens and some supermarkets. Strictly speaking, it is grey mullet, rather than cod's roe, preserved in brine. It is very salty, and you need only 1–2 teaspoons to prepare taramasalata.

cod soufflés with chicory

Serves 6

150 g (5 oz) cod
900 ml (1¼ pints) milk
1 garlic clove, crushed
1 bay leaf
pinch of fennel seeds
2 tablespoons olive oil
pinch of freshly grated nutmeg
pinch of paprika
2 eggs
3 egg yolks
50 g (2 oz) butter
3 heads chicory, cut into julienne strips
2 tablespoons lemon juice
salt and pepper
chervil leaves, to garnish
grated pecorino cheese, to serve

Preparation: *15 minutes* • **cooking:** *25 minutes*

Rinse the cod under cold running water, then remove and discard the skin and any bones. Cut the fish into 3 pieces.

Place the cod in a frying pan or large saucepan. Add 250 ml (8 fl oz) of the milk, the garlic, bay leaf, fennel seeds and 1 tablespoon of the olive oil. Season with pepper and a generous pinch of nutmeg.

Bring to the boil over a low heat. As soon as the milk froths up, turn off the heat and leave to cool.

Remove the fish from the pan with a fish slice and set it aside in a colander. Bring the cooking liquid back to the boil and cook until it has reduced by half. Season the fish with paprika and flake with a fork.

Bring the remaining milk to the boil. Whisk the whole eggs and egg yolks with salt and pepper, then pour them into the milk, whisking constantly. Stir in the fish. Generously butter 6 ramekins and spoon in the fish mixture. Place the ramekins in a roasting tin and add boiling water to come halfway up their sides. Bake in a preheated oven, 200°C (400°F), Gas Mark 6, for 20 minutes.

Sprinkle the chicory with the lemon juice. Heat the remaining olive oil in a large, heavy-based frying pan and cook the chicory over a low heat, stirring occasionally, for 5 minutes.

Remove the ramekins from the roasting tin and run a knife blade around the edges. Leave to stand for 2–3 minutes, then invert each ramekin on to a serving plate. Arrange a little chicory around each soufflé, pour over a little of the reduced cooking liquid and garnish with chervil. Sprinkle with grated pecorino and serve immediately.

fish soup

Serves 4

2 tomatoes
5 potatoes
2 onions
10 small carrots
½ head of celery
3 tablespoons olive oil
1 large sea bream, cleaned
2 medium red mullet, cleaned
1 small scorpion fish, cleaned
2 tablespoons rice
2 eggs
4 tablespoons lemon juice
coarse sea salt and pepper

To Serve

olive oil
lemon
sea salt

Preparation: *20 minutes* • **cooking:** *40 minutes*

Place the tomatoes in a bowl and pour over boiling water to cover. Leave for 1–2 minutes, then drain, cut a cross in the stem end of each tomato, and peel of the skins. Cut into small pieces and place in a bowl. Cut the potatoes into quarters and thinly slice the onions. Cut the carrots into small batons. Separate the celery sticks and cut into small batons.

Heat 2 litres (3½ pints) water in a large saucepan. Add the olive oil and season with coarse sea salt.

When the water comes to boil, add the vegetables and cook for 30 minutes. Remove the vegetables with a slotted spoon and set aside. Add all the fish, season with salt and pepper to taste and cook for 15 minutes.

Remove the fish from the pan with a fish slice, reserving the stock. Skin the fish and remove the bones, keeping the pieces of fish as large as possible. Push the stock and the bones through a fine wire sieve into a clean pan.

Bring the stock to the boil, add the rice and cook for 10 minutes. Reserve a few of the vegetables for the garnish and pass the remainder through a food

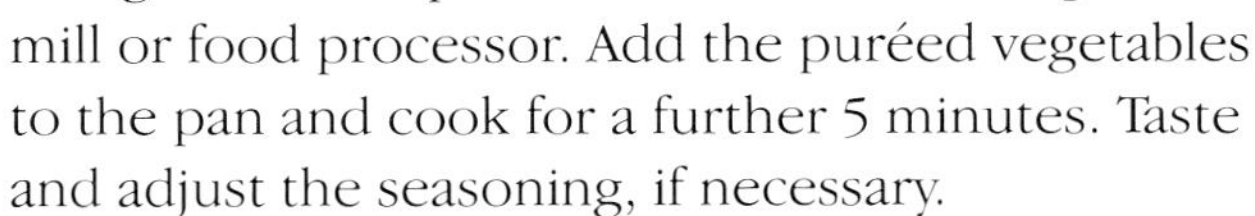

mill or food processor. Add the puréed vegetables to the pan and cook for a further 5 minutes. Taste and adjust the seasoning, if necessary.

Beat the eggs with the lemon juice, then stir in 1 tablespoon of the stock. Gradually stir in more stock, 1 tablespoon at a time, until the mixture is hot. Pour it into the pan of stock and stir well. Do not allow the soup to boil.

Serve separately – the soup first, then the fish and vegetables with olive oil, lemon and sea salt.

In ancient times, physicians were already prescribing the use of sea salt. They even rubbed their patients with it. Sea salt must be added to meat and fish just as they are served.

sea bream with aubergine purée

Serves 2

1 teaspoon coarse sea salt
3 aubergines, peeled and diced
2 garlic cloves
6 flat leaf parsley sprigs
4 tablespoons olive oil
150 g (5 oz) feta cheese, diced
½ teaspoon fennel seeds
2 small sea bream, cleaned and scaled
sea salt and pepper
dill sprigs, to garnish

Preparation: *20 minutes* • **cooking:** *40 minutes*

Bring 1 litre (1¾ pints) water to the boil in a saucepan and add the coarse sea salt. Add the aubergines, cover and simmer for 5 minutes. Drain thoroughly and squeeze out any excess water.

Chop the garlic with the parsley. Pour 2 tablespoons of the olive oil into an ovenproof dish, add the aubergines, garlic and parsley mixture and the feta and drizzle with 1 tablespoon of the remaining olive oil. Season with salt and pepper to taste and cook in a preheated oven, 150°C (300°F), Gas Mark 2, for 30 minutes.

Meanwhile, sprinkle the fennel seeds inside the cavities of the sea bream and place the fish on a flameproof dish. Drizzle with the remaining olive oil and season with salt and pepper.

When the aubergines are nearly ready, cook the sea bream under a preheated grill for 2–4 minutes on each side, until the flesh flakes easily. Sprinkle with a little sea salt, garnish with dill sprigs and serve immediately with the aubergine purée.

Sea bream, also known simply as bream, are widely available all year round.

Sea bream wrapped in spinach with spinach risotto

Serves 2

250 g (8 oz) spinach
2 small tomatoes
2 sea bream fillets
2 tablespoons natural yogurt
2 thyme sprigs, chopped
1 bay leaf
salt and pepper

For the risotto

1 tomato
2 tablespoons olive oil
50 g (2 oz) spinach, chopped
1 small onion, chopped
100 g (3½ oz) rice
2 tablespoons lemon juice
salt and pepper
Greek yogurt, to serve

Preparation: *30 minutes* • **cooking:** *25 minutes*

First, make the risotto. Place the tomato in a bowl and pour over boiling water to cover. Leave for 1–2 minutes, then drain, cut a cross in the stem end, and peel off the skin. Chop the flesh.

Heat the olive oil in saucepan. Add the spinach, stir well, then add the onion and tomato and season with salt and pepper.

Add the rice and stir in 250 ml (8 fl oz) water. Bring to the boil, then lower the heat and simmer for 15–20 minutes, until cooked. Remove from the heat and sprinkle with the lemon juice.

Meanwhile, prepare the fish. Bring a pan of salted water to the boil. Add the spinach and cook for 1 minute. Drain thoroughly, squeeze out any excess moisture and pat dry with kitchen paper.

Place the tomatoes in a bowl and pour over boiling water to cover. Leave for 1–2 minutes, then drain, cut a cross in the stem end of each tomato, and peel off the skins. Cut them in half, deseed and finely chop the flesh. Spread out the spinach leaves, side by side, in an ovenproof dish. Season the fish with salt and pepper.

Place the fish on the spinach, spoon over the yogurt, sprinkle with the thyme and add the bay leaf and chopped tomatoes. Fold the uncovered spinach leaves over the fish. Bake in a preheated oven, 230°C (450°F), Gas Mark 8, for 10 minutes.

Serve the fish with risotto, accompanied by Greek yogurt.

Fish has always been extremely important to the Cretan civilization. Minoan wax seals are decorated with figures of octopus, tuna, dolphins and sea bream. Archaeologists have even discovered a piece of pottery representing a sea bream, that was part of a vessel used to preserve the fish.

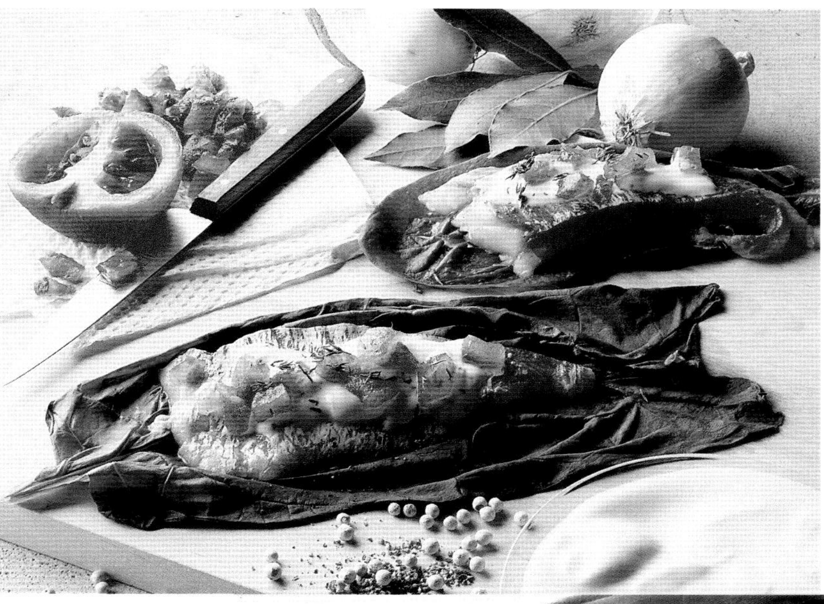

prawns spyros

SERVES 6

3 ripe tomatoes
pinch of sugar
2 tablespoons olive oil
dash of Tabasco sauce
24 raw Mediterranean or other large prawns, peeled and deveined
1 teaspoon dried oregano
1 tablespoon crème fraîche
125 g (4 oz) feta cheese, diced
2 tablespoons ouzo or Pernod
salt and pepper

Preparation and cooking: *20 minutes*

Place the tomatoes in a bowl and pour over boiling water to cover. Leave for 1–2 minutes, then drain, cut a cross in the stem end of each tomato, and peel off the skins. Halve, deseed and chop the flesh. Place in a saucepan and season with salt, pepper and sugar. Add 1 tablespoon of the olive oil and the Tabasco. Cook over a very low heat for 5 minutes.

Heat the remaining olive oil in another saucepan. Add the prawns, sprinkle with the oregano and season with salt and pepper. Cook over high heat, stirring frequently, for 2 minutes. Transfer to a serving dish and keep warm.

Pour the crème fraîche into the saucepan and add the diced feta and tomatoes. Mix well and cook for a few seconds until heated through, then pour over the prawns.

Heat the ouzo or Pernod in a small saucepan or large ladle. At the table, pour the ouzo over the prawns and flambé them. You can accompany the prawns with a dish of steamed rice if you like. In that case, cook the rice before you cook the prawns.

Ouzo is a clear, aniseed-flavoured Greek spirit, usually served as an aperitif. If it is unavailable, use Pernod or a pastis, such as Ricard.

Orange-flavoured Scallops with Chicory

Serves 6

50 g (2 oz) butter
6 heads chicory, cut into strips
plain flour, for dusting
30 large scallops with corals
4 tablespoons olive oil
6 tablespoons orange juice
salt and pepper
dill sprigs, to garnish

Preparation and cooking: *20 minutes*

Melt the butter in a frying pan and cook the chicory over a low heat, stirring occasionally, for 5 minutes.

Spread out the flour on a plate. Add the scallops, a few at a time, and turn to coat. Shake off any excess. Heat the olive oil in a frying pan and cook the scallops for 2 minutes. Season with salt and pepper, pour in the orange juice and cook for a further 1–2 minutes, until lightly caramelized.

Place the chicory on warmed plates and arrange the scallops on top. Garnish with dill sprigs and serve immediately.

Raw chicory goes well with such cheeses as ricotta and Roquefort and with nuts. Cooked, it complements scallops and salmon.

prawns with red peppers

Serves 6

3 large red peppers
1 tablespoon olive oil
30 raw Mediterranean or other large prawns, peeled and deveined
6 tablespoons orange juice
salt and pepper

Preparation and cooking: *45 minutes*

Bring a large pan of water to the boil. Add the peppers and cook for 5 minutes, then drain, peel with a sharp knife, halve and deseed. Cut the flesh into thin strips.

Heat the olive oil in a frying pan, add the red pepper strips and season with salt and pepper. Cover and cook over a low heat for 5 minutes.

Add the prawns and orange juice to the pan and cook, uncovered, for a further 2 minutes. Season to taste with salt and pepper and serve immediately.

Cretans eat green peppers in salads. Their cuisine generally ignores red peppers but gives great importance to the harvest of the sea. This combination of prawns and red peppers is excellent. If you don't have time, you don't need to peel the peppers. In that case, cook them for 20 minutes.

kakavia

Serves 4

125 ml (4 fl oz) olive oil
1 onion, grated
2 bay leaves
4 parsley sprigs
1 rosemary sprig
1 teaspoon coarse sea salt
4 small potatoes
1 large potato, diced
4 carrots, sliced lengthways
1.5–1.75 kg (3–3½ lb) sea bream, cleaned and filleted, head reserved
pepper

To serve

olive oil
lemon juice
sea salt
crusty bread

Preparation: *30 minutes* • **cooking:** *1 hour*

Heat the olive oil in a flameproof casserole. Cook the onion over a medium heat, stirring occasionally, for about 5 minutes, until lightly browned. Add the herbs, 1 litre (1¾ pints) water and the sea salt. Bring to the boil, then add the potatoes and carrots and season with pepper. Simmer for about 15 minutes, until the vegetables are tender. Remove the potatoes and carrots with a slotted spoon, set aside and keep warm.

Add the fish head to the casserole and simmer for 30 minutes. Add the fish fillets and cook over a very low heat for 10 minutes. Do not allow to boil. Remove the fish fillets, set aside and keep warm. Strain the stock, then push it through a fine sieve with the back of a wooden spoon into a warm soup tureen. Add the cooked vegetables and fish fillets. Combine olive oil, lemon juice and sea salt to taste in a sauceboat. Serve the soup immediately with the sauce and slices of crusty bread.

Make sure that you remove the gills from the fish head before adding it to the casserole, otherwise the fish stock will taste bitter.

roasted swordfish and tian of vegetables

SERVES 6

1 tablespoon olive oil
6 swordfish steaks
½–1 teaspoon dried oregano
6 tablespoons orange juice
coarse sea salt and pepper
2 tablespoons chopped parsley, to garnish

For the vegetable tian

2 tablespoons olive oil
2 garlic cloves, chopped
2 aubergines, sliced
2 courgettes, sliced
3 tomatoes, thickly sliced
4 basil sprigs, leaves torn
1 tablespoon dried oregano
coarse sea salt and pepper

Preparation: *20 minutes* • **cooking:** *2 hours*

First, prepare the vegetable tian. Brush an ovenproof dish with a little of the oil. Sprinkle the garlic over the base, then arrange the aubergines, courgettes and tomatoes on top in an alternating pattern. Drizzle with the remaining olive oil, season with salt and pepper and sprinkle with the basil leaves and oregano. Cover the dish with foil and bake in a preheated oven, 150°C (300°F), Gas Mark 2, for 1 hour.

Uncover the vegetables and bake for 1 more hour to allow some of the cooking juices to evaporate. About 5–10 minutes before the end of the cooking time, cook the fish. Heat the olive oil in a frying pan. Cook the swordfish over a high heat for 1 minute, then season with salt and pepper and sprinkle with the oregano. Turn the fish steaks over, pour over the orange juice and cook until lightly caramelized. Leave the fish steaks to rest for a few seconds before garnishing with chopped parsley and serving with the vegetable tian.

Swordfish is widely available these days, but if you prefer, you could substitute fresh tuna or even cod steaks. A tian was originally the name of an ovenproof dish in which gratins were cooked in Provence. The word is now applied to the gratin itself.

Mullet with Herbs and aubergine gratin

Serves 4

8 grey mullet, cleaned and scaled
4 tablespoons olive oil
4 thyme sprigs
2 rosemary sprigs
2 fennel sprigs
4 parsley sprigs

For the gratin

2 large, firm aubergines, thinly sliced
2 tablespoons coarse sea salt
4 ripe tomatoes, thinly sliced
3 tablespoons olive oil
4 basil sprigs, leaves coarsely torn
125 g (4 oz) peppered pecorino, thinly sliced
salt and pepper

To serve

olive oil
lemon juice
sea salt

Preparation: *1½ hours* • **cooking:** *1 hour*

First, prepare the gratin. Place the aubergines in a colander, sprinkle with 1 tablespoon of coarse sea salt and leave to drain for 1 hour.

Place the tomatoes in another colander, sprinkle them with the remaining sea salt and leave to drain for 1 hour.

Rinse the aubergines and tomatoes and pat dry with kitchen paper. Divide 1 tablespoon of the olive oil among 4 small ovenproof dishes.

Arrange the aubergine and tomato slices alternately in the dishes and drizzle with the remaining olive oil. Sprinkle the basil leaves over the vegetables and season to taste with salt and pepper. Top with the sliced pecorino. Bake in a preheated oven, 150°C (300°F), Gas Mark 2, for 50 minutes.

Brush the fish with the olive oil, place the herbs on top and season with salt and pepper.

When the vegetable gratins are just cooked, grill the mullet under a preheated grill for 1 minute on each side, then season with salt and pepper.

Mix together a little olive oil, lemon juice and a pinch of sea salt to taste and serve with the mullet and vegetable gratins.

Grey mullet, which is not related to red mullet, is a delicious fish that is best cooked whole. It is very under-estimated, so tends to be inexpensive. If you cannot find grey mullet, substitute sea bass.

sea bass grilled with fennel

SERVES 2
750 g (1½ lb) sea bass, cleaned and scaled
pinch of aniseed
3 tablespoons olive oil
4 onions, thinly sliced
2 fennel bulbs, thinly sliced
sea salt and pepper
basil leaves, to garnish
lemon juice and olive oil, to serve (optional)

Preparation: *30 minutes* • **cooking:** *30 minutes*

Place the fish on a large plate, sprinkle the aniseed inside the cavity and drizzle with a little of the olive oil. Cover with clingfilm and place in the refrigerator until required.

Heat 1 tablespoon of the remaining olive oil in a frying pan. Cook the onions over a low heat, stirring occasionally, for about 5 minutes, until softened. Add the fennel, season with salt and pepper and cook gently for a further 5 minutes.

Spoon the fennel mixture over the base of a shallow, flameproof dish and place the sea bass on top. Season with salt and pepper and drizzle the remaining olive oil over it.

Cook under a preheated grill for about 8–10 minutes on each side.

Garnish with basil leaves and serve with a little olive oil mixed with lemon juice and seasoned with sea salt to taste, if you like.

In ancient times, aniseed had a reputation for stimulating the appetite and digestive system. Cretan aniseed was widely known. Mixed with vinegar and honey, it was also used for gargling.

Maritime Leeks

Serves 6

3 tablespoons olive oil
2 kg (4 lb) leeks, sliced
6 red mullet fillets
6 sea bream fillets
6 scallops
2 tablespoons dry vermouth
sea salt and pepper

Preparation: *30 minutes* • **cooking**: *30 minutes*

Heat 1 tablespoon of the olive oil in a frying pan, add the leeks and season with salt and pepper. Half-cover and cook over a low heat for 15 minutes.

Arrange the leeks on the bases of 6 ovenproof dishes. Arrange the fish fillets and the scallops over the leeks. Pour 1 teaspoon vermouth and 1 teaspoon olive oil over a each dish, then season with sea salt and pepper. Cover with foil and bake in a preheated oven, 200°C (400°F), Gas Mark 6, for 15 minutes. Turn off the heat, remove the foil, and leave the dishes in the oven for a further 5 minutes before serving.

Leeks sold in a supermarket are often already washed, but those from farmer's markets and many greengrocers contain quite a lot of soil, so they must be washed very thoroughly under cold running water.

Sardines stuffed with pine nuts and spinach tian

Serves 6

3 garlic cloves, crushed
25 g (1 oz fresh white breadcrumbs
75 g (3 oz) pine nuts
3 tablespoons olive oil
8 sardines, cleaned and scaled
3–4 thyme sprigs
2 bay leaves
1 small bunch of parsley
salt and pepper

For the spinach tian

750 g (1½ lb) spinach, finely chopped
3 garlic cloves
6 parsley sprigs
1 tablespoon plain flour
300 ml (½ pint) milk
pinch of freshly grated nutmeg
1 tablespoon olive oil
1 teaspoon salt
50 g (2 oz) grated pecorino cheese
pepper

Preparation: *30 minutes* • **cooking:** *40 minutes*

Mix together the garlic, breadcrumbs, pine nuts and olive oil in a bowl. Season with salt and pepper.

Stuff the sardines with the breadcrumb mixture. Place the thyme and bay leaves in an ovenproof dish and top with the sardines.

To make the tian, place the spinach in a large ovenproof dish.

Chop the garlic with the parsley. Mix the flour with the milk, adding a little nutmeg and the olive oil. Combine the milk mixture with the garlic and parsley and pour over the spinach. Season with the salt and pepper to taste and sprinkle with the cheese.

Bake the spinach tian on the the bottom shelf of a preheated oven, 180°C (350°F), Gas Mark 4, for 20 minutes.

Increase the oven temperature to 200°C (400°F), Gas Mark 6, and bake for a further 5 minutes, then place the sardines on the top shelf of the oven and bake for 15 minutes. Keep an eye on the sardines and, if necessary, cover them with foil to prevent them from burning.

In Rome, people ate sardines as a starter to stimulate the appetite and facilitate digestion. Like cucumbers, sardines were considered to belong in the category of the gustatio *– they lined the stomach before the feast. In the Middle Ages, they boiled sardines and ate them with mustard.*

aubergine-wrapped salmon and tomato coulis

Serves 4
about 125 ml (4 fl oz) olive oil
4 aubergines, thinly sliced lengthways
2 semi-dry rounds of goat's cheese
1 savory sprig, chopped
4 × 125 g (4 oz) thin salmon fillets
salt and pepper

For the tomato coulis
4 large, ripe tomatoes
pinch of sugar
3 fresh basil leaves, coarsely torn
coarse sea salt and pepper

Preparation and cooking: *10 minutes*

Place the tomatoes in a bowl and pour over boiling water to cover. Leave for 1–2 minutes, then drain, cut a cross in the stem end of each tomato, and peel off the skins. Cut them in half and deseed. Put the tomato halves into a colander, sprinkle with sea salt and leave them to drain.

Heat half the olive oil in a large frying pan. Add the aubergine slices, in batches, season with salt and pepper and cook for 5 minutes on each side. Remove with a fish slice and drain on kitchen paper. Add more olive oil to the pan, as required.

Place the drained tomatoes in a blender or food processor and process to a purée. Scrape into a bowl and mix with sugar and pepper to taste and, if necessary, a little salt. Sprinkle over the basil leaves..

Cut the cheese rounds in half; season with salt and pepper and sprinkle with the savory. Place a cheese portion on each of the salmon fillets and fold the salmon over.

Wrap each salmon fillet with a few slices of aubergine and tie in place with kitchen string.

Heat 1 tablespoon of olive oil in a frying pan. Add the aubergine-wrapped salmon and cook over a low heat for 3 minutes on each side. Turn off the heat. Leave the salmon parcels on the hob for 1 more minute with the heat off. Serve the salmon surrounded with the tomato coulis.

Except for the salmon, all the ingredients in this recipe are Cretan. It would be a shame, however, to deprive ourselves of this excellent fish which protects our hearts with its omega-3 fatty acids.

red snapper parcels and tomato gratin

SERVES 2

500 g (1 lb) red snapper, cleaned and scaled
2 tablespoons olive oil
1 garlic clove
3-4 parsley sprigs
6 small vine tomatoes

Preparation: *10 minutes* • **cooking:** *40 minutes*

Cut a piece of foil large enough to enclose the fish completely. Place the fish on the foil, season with salt and pepper, drizzle with the olive oil and fold over the foil, twisting the edges to secure it. Place the parcel on a baking sheet.

Bake on the bottom shelf of a preheated oven, 200°C (400°F), Gas Mark 6, for 40 minutes.

Meanwhile, chop the garlic with the parsley. Arrange the tomatoes in a single layer in an ovenproof dish that is just large enough to hold them. Sprinkle with the mixture of garlic and parsley.

About 15 minutes before the fish is ready, place the dish of tomatoes on the top shelf of the oven. Serve the fish in its foil parcel with the tomatoes.

This recipe requires little preparation. Light and aromatic with seasoning, it limits the unpleasant odours of the cooking – as well as the washing up.

tuna 'costes' and courgette tian

Serves 6

6 × 125 g (4 oz) tuna steaks
1 bunch of coriander
1 tablespoon crushed coriander seeds
1 tablespoon olive oil
sea salt

For the courgette tian

2 tablespoons olive oil
2 kg (4 lb) courgettes, peeled and sliced
250 g (8 oz) feta cheese, diced
pinch of freshly grated nutmeg
150 ml (¼ pint) milk

Preparation: *30 minutes* • **cooking:** *45 minutes*

First, prepare the courgettes. Heat 1 tablespoon of the olive oil in a frying pan and fry the courgettes until golden brown. Season with salt and pepper, cover and cook for a further 15 minutes. Drain the courgettes in a colander.

Pour the remaining olive oil into an ovenproof dish. Spread half of the courgettes over the base, then add half the diced feta cheese and sprinkle with a little nutmeg. Layer with the remaining courgettes and cheese. Pour over the milk. Bake in a preheated oven, 180°C (350°F), Gas Mark 4, for 30 minutes.

About 3–5 minutes before the tian is ready, sear the tuna in a nonstick frying pan or griddle for 2 minutes, then season with salt and pepper. Place the tuna on warm plates and sprinkle with chopped coriander and coriander seeds. Drizzle ½ teaspoon of olive oil and sprinkle a pinch of sea salt over each tuna steak. Serve immediately with the courgette tian.

Coriander seeds contribute to the flavour of Cretan cooking as much as olive oil. You can, according to your taste, enhance the aroma of your cooking by increasing the quantity of fresh coriander.

Squid with Spinach

Serves 4

1 kg (2 lb) squid
4 tablespoons olive oil
1 onion, chopped
200 ml (7 fl oz) white wine
1 tablespoon tomato purée
2 tablespoons chopped parsley
1.5 kg (3 lb) spinach
salt and pepper

Preparation: *45 minutes* • **cooking:** *25 minutes*

Clean the squid by firmly pulling off the heads. The entrails will come away with it. Cut off the tentacles and discard the beak. Remove and discard the quill. Rinse the tentacles and the body sacs, rubbing off any skin. Cut the body sacs into thick rings. Leave the tentacles whole or chop them if you prefer.

Heat the olive oil in a large frying pan or flameproof casserole and cook the onion over a medium heat, stirring occasionally, for about 5 minutes, until browned. Increase the heat to high, add the squid and cook for several seconds, until browned. Add the wine, tomato purée and parsley, lower the heat and simmer for 10 minutes. Add the spinach and cook for a further 10 minutes. Season with salt and pepper to taste and serve.

This typical recipe combines two basic foods of the Cretan diet - spinach and squid. These two are part of the 'landscape' of the island. Squid - and its cousin cuttlefish - are very often strung up on a wire, in the same way as tomatoes, and left outside to dry in the hot air and sunshine.

rack of lamb with baby vegetables

Serves 8 to 9

1 × 2 kg (4 lb) rack of lamb
6 garlic cloves
4-5 thyme sprigs
3 tablespoons olive oil
6 carrots, cut into chunks
6 baby turnips
12 small potatoes
4 tablespoons lemon juice
salt and pepper
chopped parsley, to garnish

Preparation: *25 minutes* • **marinating:** *30 minutes*
cooking: *40 minutes*

Oil a large roasting tin, place the rack of lamb in the middle and surround it with the unpeeled garlic. Sprinkle with salt, pepper and thyme leaves. Pour olive oil evenly over the lamb and set aside to marinate for 30 minutes.

Arrange the carrots, turnips and potatoes around the meat and sprinkle with the lemon juice. Season with salt and pepper and roast in a preheated oven, 200°C (400°F), Gas Mark 6, for about 40 minutes.

Turn off the heat, open the oven door and leave the meat in the oven to rest for 10 minutes. Just before serving, sprinkle with chopped parsley.

The new season's garlic arrives in the shops in June and tastes wonderful. If it is cooked unpeeled, it becomes soft. Squeeze the roasted garlic cloves into the vegetable medley to give it a subtle and sweet flavour. The therapeutic properties of garlic have been recognized for centuries.

Lamb with bulgar wheat

Serves 6

250 g (8 oz) bulgar wheat
3 tablespoons olive oil
4 onions, thinly sliced
1 teaspoon ground cinnamon
1 teaspoon ground cumin
6 whole cloves
6 cardamom pods, crushed
1 bay leaf
1 leg of lamb, cut into pieces
300 ml (½ pint) goat's milk yogurt
pinch of paprika
3 garlic cloves
125 g (4 oz) black olives
125 ml (4 fl oz) lemon juice
salt and pepper
mint leaves, cut into thin strips to garnish

Preparation: *10 minutes* • **soaking:** *24 hours*
cooking: *25 minutes* (see photographs on page 59)

On the day before you intend to serve, place the bulgar wheat in a bowl, add cold water to cover and leave to soak.

The next day heat the olive oil in a large pan and cook the onions over a medium heat, stirring occasionally, for about 5 minutes, until browned.

Add the cinnamon, cumin, cloves, crushed cardamom and the bay leaf and mix well.

Add the meat, yogurt, paprika, unpeeled garlic and the olives. Season with salt and pepper. Lower the heat, cover and simmer for 15 minutes.

Cover the meat with the bulgar wheat (drained if necessary) and pour over the lemon juice. Taste and adjust the seasoning, if necessary. Re-cover the pan and cook for a further 5 minutes. Sprinkle the mint over the meat and serve.

The flavour of the meat is subtly enhanced in this recipe by the cloves and the cardamom seeds from the crushed pods.

Lamb with Sugar Snap Peas

Serves 4

4 tablespoons olive oil
6 garlic cloves
3 thyme sprigs
1 rosemary sprig
½ saddle of lamb
1 teaspoon ground cinnamon
1 teaspoon ground cumin
500 g (2 lb) sugar snap peas
salt and pepper

Preparation: *15 minutes* • **cooking:** *50 minutes*

Pour 1 tablespoon of the olive oil into an ovenproof dish or roasting tin. Season with salt and pepper and add the unpeeled garlic, thyme and rosemary sprigs. Place the meat on the herbs. Season the meat with salt and pepper, the cinnamon and cumin and pour the remainder of the olive oil over it.

Roast in a preheated oven, 180°C (350°F), Gas Mark 4, for 40 minutes, occasionally basting the meat with the cooking juices.

Blanch the sugar snap peas in boiling water for about 3 minutes. Drain, then immediately plunge them into a bowl of iced water to prevent any further cooking.

Drain the sugar snap peas and arrange them around the meat. Roast for a further 5 minutes.

Turn off the oven and leave the meat to rest 5 minutes before serving.

Sugar snap peas have flat sides and a beautiful green colour. You can eat the whole vegetable. The flavour is enhanced by cumin and cinnamon.

Leg of Lamb with aubergine compote

SERVES 6–8

4 tablespoons lemon juice
18 artichoke hearts
1 leg of lamb, boned and cut into 18 pieces
3 thyme sprigs
5 tablespoons olive oil
4 onions, chopped
4 aubergines, diced
8 parsley sprigs
2 bay leaves
6 garlic cloves
salt and pepper

Preparation: *10 minutes* • **cooking:** *40 minutes*

Bring a large pan of water to the boil, add the lemon juice and drop in the artichoke hearts. Bring back to the boil, then lower the heat and simmer for 5 minutes.

Remove them from the pan with a slotted spoon, plunge into iced water to prevent any further cooking, then drain.

Trim off any excess fat from the meat. Season the lamb with salt and pepper and sprinkle over the thyme leaves.

Heat 2 tablespoons of the olive oil in a large saucepan. Add the lamb and cook, stirring frequently, until browned all over. Using a slotted spoon, transfer to a platter.

Add the remaining olive oil to the saucepan. Cook the onions for a few seconds, then season with salt and pepper.

Add the aubergines, mix well and cook for several minutes so that some of the vegetable liquid evaporates. Season with salt and pepper.

Add two sprigs of parsley, the bay leaves and the unpeeled garlic to the saucepan. Return the meat to the pan and cover with the artichoke hearts. Cover the pan, lower the heat and cook gently for 30–40 minutes, until the meat is tender.

Place some lamb in the centre of each serving plate, surround it with the artichoke hearts filled with the mixture of onions and aubergines. Garnish with the remaining parsley.

This dish can be served with a rice pilaf flavoured with ground turmeric. Its beautiful golden shade would add appealing colour to this recipe. In this case, use 500-750 g (1-1½ lb) basmati rice.

Youvetsi

Serves 6

500 g (1 lb) tomatoes
500 g (1 lb) dried pasta, such as fusilli or tubetini
150 ml (¼ pint) olive oil
1.75 kg (3½ lb) free-range chicken, jointed or 6 chicken portions
1 teaspoon coarse sea salt
1 large onion, finely chopped
200 ml (7 fl oz) white wine
2 bay leaves
1 cinnamon stick
50 g (2 oz) Parmesan or pecorino cheese, grated
salt and pepper

Preparation: *30 minutes* • **cooking:** *45 minutes*

Place the tomatoes in a bowl and pour over boiling water to cover. Leave for 1–2 minutes, then drain, cut a cross in the stem end of each tomato, and peel off the skins. Halve, deseed and finely chop the flesh.

Bring a large pan of water to the boil. Add a pinch of salt and the pasta, bring back to the boil, stir and cook for 8–10 minutes, until *al dente*. Drain, cool under running water and drain again. Tip into a bowl and toss with 2 tablespoons of the olive oil.

Heat the remaining olive oil in a large pan. Season the chicken with the sea salt and pepper and brown it for 5 minutes on all sides. Add the tomatoes, onion, white wine, bay leaves and cinnamon. Cover and simmer gently for 20–30 minutes. Remove the chicken from the pan with a slotted spoon.

Place the pasta in a large ovenproof dish, add the sauce, taste and adjust the seasoning, if necessary, and mix well. Place the chicken on top and sprinkle over the grated cheese. Cook in a preheated oven, 180°C (350°F), Gas Mark 4, for 15 minutes. Check frequently and, if necessary, add a little water if the pasta is beginning to stick.

Flash the chicken under a preheated grill for a few seconds before serving.

In 1825, doctors Buchez and Trelat advised people not to overeat smoked meat. They recommended fresh poultry for good health.

kleftiko and cretan stew

Serves 6
1 small bunch of thyme
1.5 kg (3 lb) lamb shoulder
1 tablespoon olive oil
salt and pepper

For the Cretan stew
125 ml (4 fl oz) olive oil
1 teaspoon coarse sea salt
3 aubergines, sliced
3 courgettes, sliced
2 carrots, sliced
1 green pepper, halved, deseeded and thickly sliced lengthways
1 red pepper, halved, deseeded and thickly sliced lengthways
3 basil sprigs
2 garlic cloves, crushed
2 onions, thinly sliced
4 tomatoes, quartered
salt and pepper

Preparation: *1 hour* • **cooking:** *1 hour*

Put the thyme in the base of a casserole and place the lamb on top. Season with salt and pepper and drizzle with the olive oil. Cover and cook in a preheated oven, 200°C (400°F), Gas Mark 6, for 45 minutes.

Meanwhile, prepare the Cretan stew: put 4 tablespoons of the olive oil and the sea salt in an ovenproof dish and layer the aubergines, courgettes, carrots and peppers, drizzling olive oil on each layer of vegetables. Add the whole basil leaves and garlic.

Heat 1 tablespoon of the remaining olive oil in a saucepan and cook the onions for about 5 minutes, until softened. Spoon them on top of the vegetables. Add the tomatoes, season with salt and pepper and drizzle with the remaining olive oil.

When the lamb has been cooking for 45 minutes, lower the oven temperature to 180° C (350°F), Gas Mark 4, and put the vegetables in the oven. Cook for a further 15 minutes, then serve the lamb and Cretan stew.

According to legend, two robbers stole a lamb, which is how the name of the dish came to be – kleftikos *meaning stolen. One thief carried the lamb on his shoulder while the other one skinned it. The thieves descended towards the shore, washed the lamb in sea water, turned its legs toward its stomach, dug a hole in the sand, put the lamb in the hole, covered it with branches and lit a fire. The theft was thus hidden and, since the lamb was cooked covered, the flavour was preserved.*

Leg of Lamb with Peppers and Spices

Serves 8

3 tablespoons olive oil
1 teaspoon coarse sea salt
5 red or yellow peppers, halved, deseeded and cut into thin strips
1 bay leaf
10 whole cloves
8 cardamom pods
1 × 2 kg (4 lb) leg of lamb
6 garlic cloves
1 teaspoon ground cinnamon
1 teaspoon ground cumin
1 teaspoon ground coriander
1 teaspoon paprika
1 teaspoon oregano
4 tablespoons lemon juice
pepper
chopped parsley, to garnish

Preparation: *30 minutes* • **cooking:** *40 minutes*

Pour 1 tablespoon of the olive oil into a roasting tin, sprinkle with the sea salt and pepper. Arrange the red or yellow peppers, bay leaf, cloves and cardamom in the roasting tin.

Put the leg of lamb on top and arrange the unpeeled garlic around it. Sprinkle with the cinnamon, cumin, coriander, paprika and oregano and drizzle with the remaining olive oil and lemon juice.

Roast in a preheated oven, 220°C (425°F), Gas Mark 7, for 40 minutes. Turn off the heat, open the door and leave the meat in the oven for a further 10 minutes. Serve garnished with chopped parsley.

In the sixteenth century, physicians did not hesitate to prescribe garlic for the prevention of ills. Apparently, Parisians ate so much garlic during the month of May that the air was laden with the smell of it.

chicken paupiettes with goat's cheese and mint

SERVES 5

6 semi-dry goat's cheese rounds
1 bunch of fresh mint, chopped
1 piece of caul fat or 10 rashers rindless back bacon
1 × 1.75 kg (3½ lb) chicken, boned (ask your butcher to do this)
375 g(12 oz) fresh pasta
few drops of olive oil
150 ml (¼ pint) yogurt
salt and pepper

Preparation: *20 minutes* • **cooking:** *30 minutes*

Place the cheese in a bowl. Reserve a little mint for the garnish, add the remainder to the bowl and mix well. Season with salt and pepper.

Spread out the caul fat if using, on a work surface. Stretch the bacon rashers, if using, with a knife and spread out on the work surface in pairs. Cut the chicken into 5 pieces. Put 1 round of minted cheese in the middle of each piece and wrap each piece with the caul fat, cutting to fit, or with 2 bacon rashers. Secure the bacon with cocktail sticks. Reserve 1 cheese round for the sauce. Place the chicken parcels in a roasting tin.

Roast in a preheated oven, 200°C (400°F), Gas Mark 6, for 30 minutes.

Bring a large pan of lightly salted water to the boil and add a few drops of olive oil. Add the pasta, bring back to the boil and cook for 2–3 minutes or according to the packet instructions, until *al dente*. Drain and divide among 5 plates. Place a paupiette of chicken on top of each and keep warm.

Mix the remaining goat's cheese with the yogurt. Place a saucepan over a low heat. Pour in the yogurt mixture and stir well until melted and smooth, scraping the base of the pan. Before serving, sprinkle with the reserved mint, then pour the yogurt sauce over the chicken and pasta and serve.

Caul fat is a thin membrane of fat that was once widely used for wrapping around sausagemeat and larding many delicate dishes. It must be soaked before use to make it pliable. It is not readily available, although specialist butchers may be able to order it for you, if you want to make an authentic Cretan dish. Stretched bacon makes a good substitute, adding a similar pork flavour to the meat. If you prefer, you can substitute rabbit portions for the chicken.

Veal escalopes with pine nuts and roasted tomatoes

Serves 6

6 thin veal escalopes
250 ml (8 fl oz) milk
pinch of freshly grated nutmeg
6 walnut-size balls of bread without crusts
4 parsley sprigs
2 garlic cloves
2 shallots
2 tablespoons grated Gruyère cheese
50 g (2 oz) pine nuts
1 tablespoon olive oil
salt and pepper

For the garnish

1 garlic clove
4 parsley sprigs
1 tablespoon olive oil
6 large tomatoes, halved
pinch of sugar
salt and pepper

Marinating: *1 hour* • **preparation:** *2 hours*
cooking: *30 minutes*

Place the veal in a shallow ovenproof dish, season with salt and pepper, pour over the milk, add a pinch of nutmeg and set aside to marinate for 1 hour.

Soak the bread balls in a little warm water.

Chop the parsley, garlic and shallots together.

To prepare the garnish, chop the garlic with the parsley. Brush an ovenproof dish with a little of the oil and arrange the tomatoes in it. Pour 1 drop of olive oil on each tomato half; add a pinch of sugar, season with salt and pepper and top with a little of the chopped garlic and parsley mixture.

Drain the bread balls and squeeze out any excess moisture. Mix together the shallot mixture, Gruyère, bread balls and pine nuts to make a stuffing.

Drain the veal and pat dry. Spread the stuffing on each piece of veal, roll up the escalopes and place, seam side down, in an oiled ovenproof dish.

Put the two dishes in a preheated oven, 200°C (400°F), Gas Mark 6, placing the tomatoes on the top shelf, and cook for 30 minutes.

It is worth preparing a large dish of tomatoes because they will be good even the next day - they will become caramelized from the cooked sugar. Just break eggs over the leftovers and put them under the grill for a great snack.

Chicken with Lemon and Potatoes

Serves 6

1 × 2 kg (4 lb) free-range chicken
4 tablespoons olive oil
4 tablespoons lemon juice
3–4 thyme sprigs
12 small waxy potatoes
salt and pepper
chopped parsley, to garnish

Marinating: *several hours* • **preparation:** *15 minutes*
cooking: *45 minutes*

Put the chicken in a roasting tin. Mix together the olive oil, lemon juice and thyme leaves in a jug, season with salt and pepper and pour over the chicken. Set aside to marinate for at least 2 hours.

Arrange the potatoes around the chicken. Roast in a preheated oven, 180°C (350°F), Gas Mark 4, for 45 minutes, until the chicken is cooked through and the potatoes are puffed up. Test the chicken by inserting a skewer into the thickest part; if the juices run clear with no hint of pink, then it is ready. If necessary, raise the oven temperature and cook the chicken for a little longer.

Before serving, sprinkle the plate with chopped parsley.

From the seventeenth to eighteenth century, everyday life was riddled with formal customs. For example, in 1690, the Duke of Aumont served 171 dishes to 42 guests. Madame de Sévigné, however, led a 'simple' life in Rochers. Her preference was for natural foods and she would choose lamb and chicken rather than beef. Without realizing it, she chose the Cretans' favoured meats.

pork with Leeks

Serves 6–8

2 tablespoons olive oil
1 onion, chopped
2 kg (4 lb) leeks, sliced
pinch of freshly grated nutmeg
1 kg (2 lb) boneless pork loin, cut into small pieces
3 sage leaves
salt and pepper

Preparation: *25 minutes* • **cooking**: *30 minutes*

Heat 1 tablespoon of the olive oil in a large frying pan. Cook the onion over a low heat, stirring occasionally, for 5 minutes, until softened. Add the leeks and nutmeg and season with salt and pepper. Cook for a further 5 minutes. Add the remaining olive oil, the pork and sage.

Cover and cook gently for about 20 minutes. Halfway through the cooking time, uncover the pan to allow some of the cooking juices to evaporate.

According to Claude Galen, a famous Roman physician, leek is 'light', while pork is 'heavy'. The sum total of this recipe is, therefore, 'equilibrium'.

quail with cabbage and juniper berries

Serves 4

1 Savoy cabbage, quartered
4 quails
50–75 g (2–3 oz) raisins
1 tablespoon olive oil
8 juniper berries
4 sage leaves
salt and pepper

Preparation: *15 minutes* • **cooking:** *30 minutes*

Bring a large pan of lightly salted water to the boil. Add the cabbage and cook for 5 minutes, then remove with a slotted spoon and place in a colander to drain well.

Stuff the cavities of the quails with the raisins, reserving a few for the garnish, and season with salt and pepper. Heat the olive oil in a large, flameproof casserole and cook the quails, turning frequently, for about 5 minutes, until browned on all sides. Season with salt and pepper. Remove the casserole from the heat.

Remove and discard the core from the cabbage, then cut into thin strips. Cover the quails with half of the cabbage strips, add the reserved raisins, the juniper berries and sage. Top with the rest of the cabbage and season with salt and pepper. Cover the casserole and cook in a preheated oven, 220°C (425°F), Gas Mark 7, for 20–25 minutes.

Serve each quail on a bed of cabbage.

Once a game bird, quail is now farmed and widely available, fresh or frozen, from butchers and supermarkets. It is a fairly small bird, weighing 125–150 g (4–5 oz), but is quite meaty. Cooking it with the cabbage prevents it from drying out. If quail is not available, use 2 poussins instead,

poussins with walnuts and poppy seed crêpes

SERVES 4
2 tablespoons olive oil
3-4 thyme sprigs
1 bay leaf
4 small poussins
1 tablespoon white wine vinegar
500 g (1 lb) grapes
8 fresh walnuts, shelled

For the crêpes
1 egg
1 egg yolk
100 g (3½ oz) plain flour
250 ml (8 fl oz) milk
50 g (2 oz) poppy seeds
1 tablespoon olive oil
salt and pepper

Marinating: *1 hour* • **preparation:** *25 minutes*
resting: *1 hour* • **cooking:** *40 minutes*

Brush a roasting tin with a little of the oil, sprinkle with the thyme leaves and add the bay leaf. Place the poussins in it, drizzle with the remaining oil and the vinegar and set aside to marinate for 1 hour.

Deseed the grapes with the point of a knife over a bowl to catch the juice. Leave the grape seeds in the juice and add the walnuts.

Prepare the batter for the crêpes. Beat the whole egg and yolk with the flour in a bowl. Season with salt and pepper and beat in the milk and poppy seeds. Cover and set aside to rest for 1 hour.

Roast the poussins in a preheated oven, 230°C (450°F), Gas Mark 8, for 40 minutes.

To cook the crêpes, heat a little olive oil in a crêpe pan and stir the batter. Pour about half a ladle of the batter into the pan and tilt the pan to coat the base evenly. Cook over a low heat for 1 minute, until the underside is golden and the crêpe is set. Flip over and cook the other side for 1 minute. Slide out on to a plate and keep warm while you cook the rest of the crêpes.

About 5 minutes before the poussins finish cooking, add the grapes and the walnuts to the roasting tin.

You may serve the crêpes separately or place them around the poussins.

Poussins, also known as spring chicken, are ideal for single servings.
In Crete, young pigeons, or squab, would also be prepared in this way.

Avgolemono Soup and Chicken Salad

SERVES 4

1 teaspoon coarse sea salt
1 kg (2 lb) chicken portions
100 g (3½ oz) rice
2 eggs
125 ml (4 fl oz) lemon juice, plus extra to serve
50 g (2 oz) Parmesan or pecorino cheese
4 tablespoons olive oil
125 g (4 oz) shelled broad beans
50 g (2 oz) unpeeled almonds
1 tablespoon balsamic vinegar
6 saffron threads
6 walnuts, shelled
4 ready-to-eat dried apricots, halved
500 g (1 lb) tomatoes, quartered
250 g (8 oz) mixed salad leaves
6 mint sprigs
salt and pepper

Preparation: *30 minutes* • **cooking:** *30 minutes*

Bring 1 litre (1¾ pints) water to the boil in a pan and add the sea salt. Add the chicken portions, season with pepper and simmer for 25 minutes, or until tender. Remove the chicken with a slotted spoon.

Bring the water back to the boil, add the rice and cook for 10–20 minutes, until tender.

Beat the eggs with salt and pepper. Gradually beat in the lemon juice, then ladle in the stock from the pan, a little at a time, whisking constantly to obtain a smooth, thick, sauce-like soup. Grate half the cheese. Serve the soup with the grated cheese and lemon juice seasoned with a few drops of olive oil.

Cook the beans and almonds in lightly salted, boiling water for 5 minutes. Drain and remove the skins from both.

Prepare a dressing by mixing the remaining olive oil, balsamic vinegar and saffron, then season to taste with salt and pepper.

Cut meat from the chicken portions and place in a bowl with the beans, almonds, walnuts, apricots and tomatoes. Pour in half the dressing and toss.

Arrange the salad leaves on a platter, season with salt and pepper and pour over the remaining dressing. Top with the chicken salad and shave over the remaining Parmesan or pecorino. Finely shred some of the mint over the salad and garnish with whole mint leaves.

This dish is also a good way of using up leftover roast chicken or turkey.

duck with orange and pepper sauce

SERVES 4

2 red peppers
1 tablespoon olive oil
2 large duck breasts
6 tablespoons orange juice
salt and pepper
basil leaves, to garnish

Preparation: *15 minutes* • **cooking:** *15 minutes*

Bring a large pan of water to the boil, add the red peppers and cook for 5 minutes. Drain, peel, halve and deseed. Dice the flesh.

Heat the oil in a frying pan. Add the peppers, season with salt and pepper and cook over a low heat, stirring occasionally, for about 10 minutes.

Meanwhile, heat another frying pan or a griddle pan until very hot. Add the duck breasts, skin side down, and cook for 10 minutes, until the skin is well browned. Turn the duck breasts over, season with salt and pepper and cook for a further 5 minutes.

The duck breasts should be medium rare and slightly pink on the inside. Cover them with the peppers, pour over the orange juice and cook until lightly caramelized.

Slice the duck breasts thinly. Place the duck slices on one side of warmed serving plates and the peppers on the other side. Garnish with basil leaves and serve immediately.

Ducks are not a typically Cretan ingredient. However, because they are rich in some fatty acids, we can integrate them into the Cretan diet and, what's more, they are delicious and easy to prepare.

chicken with thyme crust and polenta cake

Serves 6
3 tablespoons olive oil
6 tablespoons grapefruit juice
1 teaspoon sea salt
3-4 thyme sprigs, chopped
1 chicken
6 tart dessert apples
2 tablespoons lemon juice
salt and pepper

For the polenta cake
pinch of freshly grated nutmeg
2 tablespoons olive oil
200 g (7 oz) polenta
1 tablespoon butter
50 g (2 oz) Parmesan cheese
¼ teaspoon sesame seeds
2 parsley sprigs, chopped
salt and pepper

Marinating: *2-3 hours* • **preparation:** *30 minutes*
cooking: *40 minutes*

Mix together the olive oil and grapefruit juice in a jug. Pour half the mixture into a large roasting tin. Season with half the sea salt and pepper to taste and add half the chopped thyme. Place the chicken flat in the tin, pour over the remaining grapefruit mixture, sprinkle with the remaining thyme and season with the remaining sea salt and pepper to taste. Cover and set aside to marinate for 2–3 hours.

Peel the apples, cut them in half from top to bottom and core, then immediately sprinkle with the lemon juice to prevent discoloration.

Roast the chicken in a preheated oven, 180°C (350°F), Gas Mark 4, for 1 hour.

Meanwhile, prepare the polenta cake: Bring 1 litre (1¾ pints) water to the boil in a large pan over a high heat. Season well with salt and pepper and add the nutmeg and olive oil. Lower the heat so that the water is simmering, then gradually add the polenta in a steady stream, stirring constantly until thickened, but do not allow it to become dry.

Remove the pan from the heat, stir in the butter and grate in half the Parmesan. Pour the mixture into an oiled cake or loaf tin or terrine. Shave the remaining Parmesan over the top and garnish with the sesame seeds and chopped parsley. Cover and set aside.

When the chicken has been cooking for 1 hour, arrange the apples, cut sides up, around the bird and move the roasting tin to a lower shelf.

At the same time, place the polenta cake on the top shelf. Cook for a further 10 minutes and serve immediately.

You could also prepare game birds, such as guinea fowl and young pheasant, in this way and reduce the initial roasting time by half.

fettuccine for the impatient

SERVES 2

2 tablespoons olive oil
250 g (8 oz) egg fettuccine
3 ripe tomatoes, quartered
6 basil leaves, coarsely torn
1 tablespoon balsamic vinegar
coarse sea salt and pepper

Preparation: *10 minutes* • **cooking:** *2-10 minutes*

Bring a large saucepan of water to the boil and add a few drops of olive oil. Add the pasta and coarse sea salt, bring back to the boil and cook until *al dente*. This will take 2–3 minutes for fresh pasta and 8–10 minutes for dried.

Drain the pasta and toss with 1 tablespoon of the olive oil, then divide it among serving plates.

Arrange the tomatoes and the basil on the pasta; drizzle with the remaining olive oil and the vinegar and season to taste with sea salt and pepper.

When you have only a short time to prepare a meal let your imagination wander. Adding some smoked salmon or grated Parmesan cheese could turn this recipe into a one-pot meal. In 1819, Doctor Etienne Brunaud wrote about the diet of intellectuals. According to him, intellectuals have delicate stomachs and he advises them to eat certain foods, including pasta. Even at that time, some physicians were already praising the benefits of what we now call slow-release carbohydrates.

pecorino fettuccine

Serves 6

3 tablespoons olive oil
625 g (1¼ lb) egg fettuccine
1 teaspoon coarse sea salt
300 g (10 oz) peppered pecorino cheese, thinly sliced
300 ml (½ pint) natural yogurt
1 thyme sprig
few drops balsamic vinegar
12 walnuts, shelled

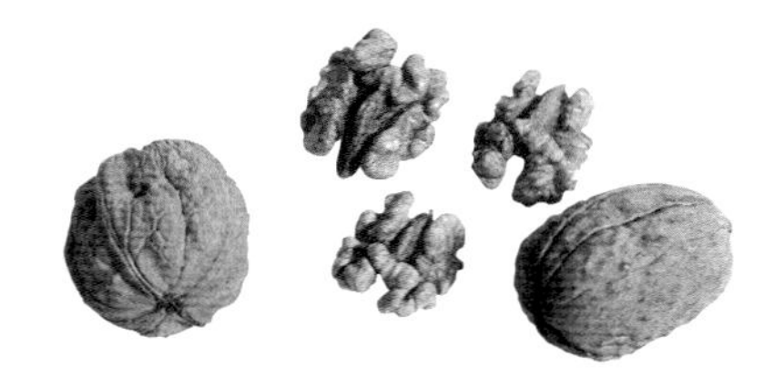

Preparation: *10 minutes* • **cooking:** *2–10 minutes*

Bring a large saucepan of water to the boil and add a few drops of olive oil. Add the pasta and sea salt, bring back to the boil and cook until *al dente*. This will take 2–3 minutes for fresh pasta and 8–10 minutes for dried.

Put the cheese into a heavy-based saucepan with the yogurt, remaining olive oil and thyme. Set over a low heat and stir well for 1 minute, until the cheese has melted and the sauce is smooth.

Drain the pasta and tip it into a warm serving bowl. Pour the sauce over it and add a few drops of vinegar. Garnish with the walnuts and serve.

Pecorino is an Italian ewe's milk cheese, made with or without peppercorns. Served with nuts, it makes a quick, nutritious and complete meal.

Spaghetti with Squid

Serves 6
1 kg (2 lb) prepared squid
2 tablespoons olive oil
2 tomatoes, halved
1 onion, chopped
1 red pepper, halved, deseeded and chopped
200 g (7oz) can tomato purée
2 garlic cloves, crushed
3 whole cloves
1 red pimiento, chopped
½ bay leaf
1 small bunch of parsley, chopped
4–6 tarragon leaves
625 g (1¼ lb) spaghetti
salt and pepper

Preparation: *30 minutes* • **cooking:** *30 minutes*

Cut the squid into strips and season with salt and pepper. Heat 1 tablespoon of the olive oil in a frying pan. Add the squid and cook over a high heat, stirring frequently, until it begins to curl. Remove with a slotted spoon and drain in a colander.

Gently squeeze the tomato halves with your fingers to remove the seeds and excess juice.

Heat the remaining olive oil and cook the chopped onion and pepper over a low heat, stirring occasionally, for about 5 minutes, until the onion has softened. Add the tomatoes, season with salt and pepper and cook for a further 5 minutes to reduce the liquid.

Add the tomato purée, garlic, drained squid, chopped pimiento, bay leaf and parsley and simmer gently for 20 minutes.

Remove from the heat and sprinkle with the tarragon leaves.

Shortly before the squid is ready, cook the spaghetti in a large pan of lightly salted, boiling water containing a few drops of olive oil for 8–10 minutes, until *al dente*.

Drain the pasta, tip it into a warm serving dish and top with the squid sauce.

The Romans believed that tarragon caused a stomach reaction. This very aromatic herb must be used sparingly. A few leaves are enough to flavour a dish.

tagliatelle with mussels

Serves 6

2 kg (4 lb) fresh mussels
3 tablespoons olive oil
2 shallots, chopped
6 parsley sprigs
1 teaspoon coarse sea salt
625 g (1¼ lb) tagliatelle
2 garlic cloves, crushed
3 tomatoes, halved and deseeded
salt and pepper

Preparation: *30 minutes* • **cooking:** *15–20 minutes*

Scrub the mussels under cold running water and pull off the beards. Discard any with damaged shells or that do not shut immediately when sharply tapped. Place them in a large saucepan with 2 tablespoons of the olive oil, the shallots and 2 parsley sprigs. Cover tightly and cook over a high heat, shaking the pan occasionally, for 4–5 minutes. As soon as the mussels open, remove them with a slotted spoon, discarding any that remain unopened. Strain the cooking liquid through a sieve lined with muslin and reserve. Shell the mussels and discard the shells.

Bring a large saucepan of water to the boil and add a few drops of olive oil. Add the sea salt and the pasta, bring back to the boil and cook until *al dente*. This will take 2–3 minutes for fresh pasta and 8–10 minutes for dried. Drain, tip into a warm serving bowl and toss with a few drops of olive oil.

Meanwhile, chop the remaining parsley. Heat the remaining olive oil in a saucepan and add the garlic, tomatoes, parsley and the reserved mussel cooking liquid. Season to taste with salt and pepper and cook for 5 minutes, until reduced. Remove from the heat, add the mussels to the pan, mix well and pour over the tagliatelle.

The less time the pasta cooks, the less is its glycemic index and the greater is the feeling of being full for a long time. Casanova followed this rule to the letter. The notorious Italian seducer knew that to be fit it is better to eat good food cooked al dente, *which means to the bite.*

Hot and cold figs

Serves 1

3 figs
1 tablespoon melted butter
1 tablespoon brown sugar
1 tablespoon sweet white wine, such as Samos, or white port
1 teaspoon ground cinnamon
1 scoop vanilla ice cream
1 mint leaf

Preparation and cooking: *5 minutes*

Slit the figs in a cross shape and open out. Place them in a saucepan with the melted butter and sugar and cook over a low heat until they caramelize.

Add the wine or port and sprinkle on the cinnamon. Bring to the boil stirring constantly.

Serve warm with a scoop of vanilla ice cream and decorate with a fresh mint leaf.

Sugar consumption first became common in the eighteenth century. Syrups were also recommended then to relieve some health problems.

martine's poached figs

Serves 6

30 ripe figs
740 ml (1¼ pints) sweet white wine, such as Samos, or white port
1 cinnamon stick
6 whole cloves
15 g (½ oz) butter
75 g (3 oz) brown sugar

Preparation: *25 minutes* • **infusing:** *24 hours*
cooking: *15 minutes*

On the day before you intend to serve, prick the figs several times with a skewer. Place in a large glass dish, pour in the wine, add the cinnamon and cloves and set aside for 24 hours.

The next day, drain the figs in a colander, reserving the wine.

Melt the butter with the sugar in a frying pan and cook the figs on all sides. Arrange them on a serving platter.

Pour the wine into a saucepan and heat until it is reduced by half, then pour it over the figs. Serve immediately.

Samos is an island wine that resembles port, which is commonly used to make this dessert. Do not fail to try this recipe – it is worthy of a cordon bleu.

figs au gratin with pine nuts

Serves 6

24 very ripe figs
15 g (½ oz) butter
125 g (4 oz) pine nuts
4 tablespoons lemon juice
75 g (3 oz) brown sugar

Preparation: *5 minutes* • **cooking:** *10 minutes*

Slit the figs in a cross shape and arrange them in a buttered ovenproof dish. Place the pine nuts inside the figs and sprinkle with the lemon juice and sugar.

Bake in a preheated oven, 180°C (350°F), Gas Mark 4, for 10 minutes.

If you are in a hurry cook the figs on the hob, but don't leave the kitchen because the pine nuts will burn.

Serve immediately.

Roman athletes nourished themselves with dried figs. A meal of figs, cheese, and walnuts allowed the athletes to sustain their efforts during training.

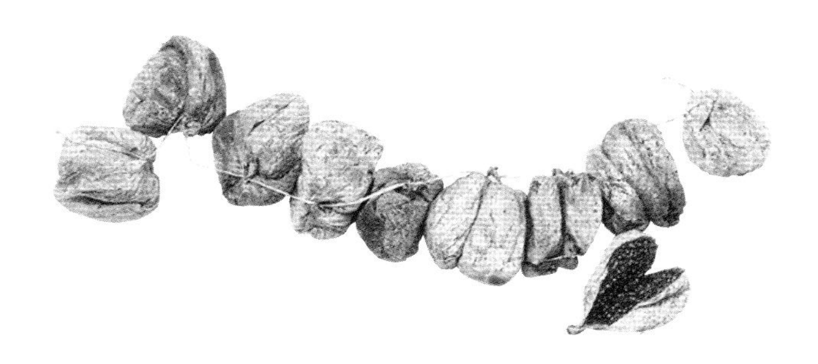

apple flan with sweet almonds and saffron

Serves 6

90 g (3½ oz) butter, melted
5 apples, peeled, cored and halved
90 g (3½ oz) ground almonds
4 tablespoons lemon juice
5 eggs
125 g (4 oz) granulated sugar
1 teaspoon potato flour
250 ml (8 fl oz) milk
½ teaspoon saffron threads

Preparation: *15 minutes* • **cooking:** *30 mint*

Brush a fluted flan tin with a little of the melted butter. Slice the apples directly into the tin. Sprinkle on 1 tablespoon of the ground almonds and drizzle with the lemon juice.

Beat the eggs with the sugar until combined. Add the potato flour and milk and mix well with a spatula. Stir in the remaining ground almonds with the remaining melted butter, mix well and pour over the apples. Sprinkle evenly with the saffron.

Bake in a preheated oven, 200°C (400°F), Gas Mark 6, for 30 minutes. Turn off the heat but leave the flan to rest in the oven. Serve warm.

In the Middle Ages, almonds were used to make soup during lean times. The almonds were peeled, crushed, soaked in warm water and boiled with spices and saffron. The resulting soup was then poured over a fried half sole in individual bowls.

caramelized apples with walnuts

Serves 6

6 apples, cored
2 tablespoons lemon juice
15 g (½ oz) butter
12 walnuts, coarsely crushed
2 tablespoons brown sugar

Preparation: *10 minutes* • **cooking:** *5 minutes*

Thinly slice each apple into rounds and immediately sprinkle with the lemon juice to prevent discoloration.

Butter an flameproof dish. Layer the nuts with the apple slices in the dish, reconstructing the apple shape. Sprinkle with the sugar.

Cook under the a preheated grill for 5 minutes, watching closely to prevent the nuts from scorching. Turn off the heat and leave the apples to rest for 5 minutes before serving.

In Rome, walnuts pickled in vinegar were prescribed for patients with jaundice. In fact, the acidity of the walnuts renders them easier to digest.

Apples with rhubarb compote

Serves 6

1 kg (2 lb) rhubarb, cut into chunks
20 g (¾ oz) butter
2 star anise
75 g (3 oz) brown sugar
6 red apples
24 raisins
½ teaspoon ground cinnamon
2 tablespoons clear honey

Preparation: *20 minutes* • **cooking:** *35 minutes*

Blanch the rhubarb in boiling water for 5 minutes, then drain well.

Butter an ovenproof dish, place the rhubarb pieces in it and arrange the star anise in the middle. Sprinkle with the sugar.

Slice off the tops and core the apples. Fill the cavities with the raisins, a pinch of cinnamon, 1 teaspoon honey, and a knob of butter. Cover with the tops and nestle the apples in the rhubarb.

Bake in a preheated oven, 200°C (400°F), Gas Mark 6, for 30 minutes. Turn off the heat and leave to rest for 5 minutes before serving.

To save time, you can use frozen rhubarb. Thaw in a colander and squeeze the chunks between your fingers to drain off any excess water.

pears with red wine

Serves 6
thinly pared rind of 1 orange
6 pears
4 tablespoons lemon juice
12 whole cloves
500 ml (17 fl oz) red wine
75 g (3 oz) brown sugar
1 cinnamon stick
1 star anise
2 tablespoons redcurrant jelly

Preparation: *30 minutes* • **cooking**: *20 minutes*
chilling: *15 minutes*

Cut the orange rind into thin strips with a sharp knife.

Peel the pears, leaving the stems attached, and immediately brush with lemon juice to prevent discoloration. Stud each pear with 2 whole cloves.

Stand the pears in a saucepan, pour in the wine and add the sugar, cinnamon, star anise and the orange rind. Cook over a low heat for 15–20 minutes, until tender, but still firm.

Carefully remove the pears with a slotted spoon. Strain the cooking liquid and discard the cinnamon stick and star anise. Reserve the orange rind. Return the cooking liquid to the pan and bring to the boil over a high heat, then boil for 5 minutes, until reduced. Stir in the redcurrant jelly.

Pour the sauce over the pears, decorate with orange rind strips and leave to rest for 15 minutes before serving.

Tannin, which gives wine its healthy, preventative attributes, is found primarily in red wine. The more tannin a wine contains, the more full-bodied it is.

pistachio pear cake

SERVES 6

90 g (3½ oz) butter
3 pears, peeled and cored
2 tablespoons lemon juice
50 g (2 oz) peeled pistachio nuts
200 g (7 oz) plain flour
1 sachet dried yeast
pinch of salt
125 g (4 oz) granulated sugar
100 ml (3½ fl oz) lukewarm milk
2 large eggs

Preparation: *15 minutes* • **cooking:** *30 minutes*

Butter an ovenproof dish. Dice the pears directly into the dish. Sprinkle with the lemon juice and pistachios.

Mix together the flour and yeast in a bowl. Add the salt, sugar and warm milk. Melt the remaining butter and pour it into the mixture. Beat the eggs, add them to the bowl and mix well with an electric mixer or balloon whisk until the batter leaves a ribbon trail when the whisk is lifted. Pour the batter evenly over the pears. Wipe any spills from the edges of the dish.

Bake in a preheated oven, 180°C (350°F), Gas Mark 4, for 30 minutes. Check to see if it is cooked through by inserting the point of a knife or a skewer in the middle of the cake. If it comes out almost dry, the cake is cooked through.

Leave the cake to cool and serve in the dish.

The doyenne-du-comice pear is an excellent autumn and early winter pear. At the end of January it is not so good, even if it looks the same. If you want to serve this dessert in the summer, use peaches and apricots instead. The pistachios give this cake a lovely nutty flavour.

grapefruit tart

Serves 6
200 g (7 oz) plain flour
100 g (3¾ oz) butter, diced
50 g (2 oz) granulated sugar
pinch of salt
1 egg yolk

For the meringue
4 egg whites
pinch of salt
1 tablespoon light brown sugar

For the cream
175 ml (6 fl oz) grapefruit juice
125 g (4 oz) granulated sugar
pinch of salt
3 tablespoons cornflour
3 egg yolks, at room temperature

Preparation: *25 minutes* • **cooking:** *30–35 minutes*

Put the flour, butter, sugar, salt and egg yolk into a food processor and process quickly to form a smooth dough.

Roll out the dough on a lightly floured surface and use to line a 23 cm (9 inch) tart tin. Prick the base and the sides with a fork, then leave to rest in the refrigerator for 30 minutes.

Bake the pastry case in a preheated oven, 200°C (400°F), Gas Mark 6, for 10–15 minutes, until firm and lightly golden.

Prepare the cream. Pour the grapefruit juice into a heavy-based saucepan. Add the sugar, salt and cornflour and mix well. Cook over a low heat, stirring constantly, until the sauce thickens. Remove from the heat, leave to cool slightly, then beat in the egg yolks one at a time. Set aside to cool.

A few minutes before the pastry case has finished baking, whisk the egg whites with the salt until soft peaks form. Pour the grapefruit cream into the pastry case. Spread the egg whites evenly over the tart with a fork. Sprinkle with the brown sugar and place for a few seconds under a preheated grill to brown the meringue.

In one of his treatises, Plutarch, the Greek moralist, dissuades us from eating desserts. A small infraction of this rule, however, has no serious consequences.

baklava and lemon granita

Serves 12

150 g (5 oz) butter
1 teaspoon ground cinnamon
150 g (5 oz) almonds, chopped
150 g (5 oz) pistachio nuts, chopped
150 g (5 oz) walnuts chopped
12 sheets of filo pastry

For the baklava syrup

375 g (12 oz) granulated sugar
3 tablespoons clear honey
1 tablespoon lemon juice
1 tablespoon orange flower water (optional)

For the granita

400 g (13 oz) granulated sugar
350 ml (12 fl oz) lemon juice

Preparation: *45 minutes* • **freezing:** *12 hours*
cooking: 1 hour *20 minutes*

Prepare the granita the day before you intend to serve. Pour 400 ml (14 fl oz) water into a heavy-based saucepan and add the sugar. Heat, stirring constantly until the sugar has dissolved, then bring to the boil. Cook over a high heat, without stirring, until the syrup is thick but not caramelized. Remove from the heat and set aside to cool.

Stir the lemon juice into the syrup. Pour the mixture into a metal or freezerproof plastic container and place in the freezer for 12 hours.

The next day, prepare the syrup for the baklava. Mix the sugar, honey, lemon juice and orange flower water, if using, with 400 ml (14 fl oz) water in a heavy-based saucepan. Bring to the boil, stirring constantly until the sugar has dissolved. Cook, without stirring, until the syrup has thickened and registers 107°C (225°F) on a sugar thermometer or has reached thread stage. Test by dipping the back of a dry teaspoon in a little syrup, press the back of another teaspoon against and pull them apart. If a fine thread forms, the syrup is ready. Set it aside to cool.

Prepare the baklava. Melt the butter, then skim off the white foam that rises to the surface. Mix the cinnamon and the nuts together.

Brush a cake tin the same size as the sheets of filo with melted butter. Place 1 sheet of filo in the tin and brush with the butter. Stack 5 more sheets on top, brushing each one with the butter. Spread the nuts over the filo. Continue to layer the sheets of filo, brushing each one with the butter, until they are all used. Brush the top sheet with the butter.

With a sharp knife, cut the top into triangles, without cutting through the filling. Sprinkle over a little water to moisten. Bake in a preheated oven, 150°C (300°F), Gas Mark 2, for 1 hour, until crisp and golden.

Remove the baklava from the oven and pour the cooled syrup over it while it is still warm.

Before serving, flake the granita with a fork and divide it among sundae glasses or bowls.

peaches with pistachios

SERVES 6

6 yellow peaches, peeled, halved and stoned
2 tablespoons lemon juice
125 g (4 oz) shelled pistachio nuts
2 tablespoons sweet white wine, such as Samos, or white port
15 g (½ oz) butter

Preparation: *10 minutes* • **cooking:** *15 minutes*

Sprinkle the peaches with the lemon juice, fill the cavities with pistachios and sprinkle with the wine or port.

Butter an ovenproof dish and arrange the peaches in it in a single layer. Bake in a preheated oven, 180°C (350°F), Gas Mark 4, for 15 minutes. Serve the peaches warm.

According to Doctor Patin, who was famous at the beginning of the seventeenth century, fruits moisten and refresh the body but don't nourish it much. It is necessary to eat juicy fruits as starters and dry ones for dessert. The former stimulate the appetite, while the latter aid digestion.

olive and aniseed bread sticks with peach granita

SERVES 6

15 g (½ oz) butter
150 g (5 oz) plain flour
75 g (3 oz) granulated sugar
pinch of salt
1 egg
125 g (4 oz) ground almonds
100 ml (3½ fl oz) olive oil
1 teaspoon aniseed
beaten egg yolk, to glaze

For the granita

200 g (7 oz) granulated sugar
4 large, white peaches, peeled, stoned and coarsely chopped
4 tablespoons lemon juice

Preparation: *30 minutes (some the previous day)*
freezing: *12 hours* • **cooking:** *28 minutes*

Prepare the granita the day before you intend to serve. Pour 150 ml (¼ pint) water into a saucepan, add the sugar and bring to the boil, stirring constantly until the sugar has dissolved. Boil, without stirring, until thickened and reduced by half, but do not allow it to caramelize. Set aside to cool.

Place the peaches in a food processor with the lemon juice and cooled syrup and process until smooth. Scrape the mixture in a metal or freezerproof plastic container and place in the freezer for 12 hours.

The next day, prepare the bread sticks. Butter and flour a baking sheet. Mix together the sugar, salt and the whole egg in a bowl. Add the remaining flour, ground almonds, olive oil and aniseed. Stir well with a wooden spatula, then work the dough by hand. Form it into a ball.

Using a teaspoon, cut and form small dough balls, then roll them into a cigar shape. Place them on the baking sheet. Make a shallow slash in the middle of each and brush them with the beaten egg yolk. Bake in a preheated oven, 200°C (400°F), Gas Mark 6, for 8 minutes.

Remove the bread sticks from the oven and transfer to a wire rack to cool. Serve cold with granita.

The peach arrived in Europe via Persia. The Roman general Lucullus (first century AD) was without a doubt instrumental in its introduction to Rome.

Honeyed Yogurt with Walnuts

Serves 2
200 ml (7 fl oz) goat's milk or Greek yogurt
1 tablespoon clear honey
4 walnuts, coarsely chopped

Preparation: *5 minutes* • **cooking:** *none*

Pour the yogurt in a bowl, pour over the honey and decorate with the nuts.
In the summer, you can replace the walnuts with fresh fruits, such as apricots, strawberries or grapes.

Pythagoras of Samos died around the year 490 BC. The famous mathematician followed a strict diet based on vegetables, dairy products and honey. According to him, music, exercise and sobriety are part of the fundamental principle of the philosophy of life.

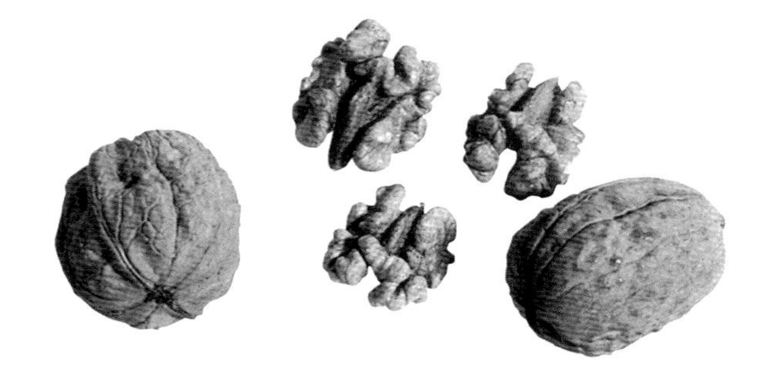

walnut oil and pine nut cake

SERVES 6

4 eggs
125 g (4 oz) granulated sugar
125 ml (4 fl oz) natural yogurt
5 tablespoons walnut oil
4 tablespoons lemon juice
1 tablespoon vanilla sugar
175 g (6 oz) plain flour
1 sachet dried yeast
15 g (½ oz) butter
3 tablespoons pine nuts
jam, to serve

Preparation: *15 minutes* • **cooking:** *40 minutes*

Beat the eggs with the granulated sugar in a bowl until combined and smooth. Pour the yogurt and walnut oil into the mixture and beat well to blend. Stir in the lemon juice and vanilla sugar.

Place the flour in another bowl and mix in the yeast. Stir in the egg mixture and mix well. When the mixture is smooth, pour it into a buttered cake tin.

Sprinkle the pine nuts over the batter and bake in a preheated oven, 140°C (275°F), Gas Mark 1, for 40 minutes.

Serve with jam.

This cake is as delicious as it is simple. The walnut oil beautifully complements the pine nuts. In ancient times, pine nuts were considered a medication. Dried pine nuts were prescribed to purge the chest and lungs.

Andrea's rice

Serves 8

6 tablespoons orange juice
125 g (4 oz) raisins
200 g (7 oz) long grain rice
2 tablespoons cornflour
1 litre (1¾ pints) milk
pinch of salt
125 g (4 oz) granulated sugar
1 vanilla pod
few drops of orange flower water (optional)
15 g (½ oz) butter
1 teaspoon ground cinnamon
1 teaspoon peeled pistachio nuts

Preparation: *15 minutes* • **cooking:** *25 minutes*

Pour the orange juice in a bowl and add the raisins. Set aside to soak.

Bring 2 litres (3½ pints) water to the boil in a large saucepan. Add the rice and boil for 5 minutes. Drain well.

Stir the cornflour with 2 tablespoons of the milk in a saucepan over a low heat. Pour the mixture into the cold milk, stir well, then return to the saucepan. Stir in the salt, sugar, vanilla pod and orange flower water and heat gently, stirring constantly.

When the milk mixture starts to boil, add the drained rice and raisins and cook over a low heat for 15 minutes. Remove from the heat, add the butter and mix well.

Remove the vanilla pod. Divide the rice among 8 bowls, sprinkle with the cinnamon, add the pistachios in the centre and leave cool.

The rice should have a velvety texture but remain moist, although it will dry slightly while cooling.

Claude Galien integrated pistachios into his 'calming diet'. Prescribed in cases of chronic diseases, his low-calorie regimen caused weakness. Pistachios compensated for this, high in calories,

indexes

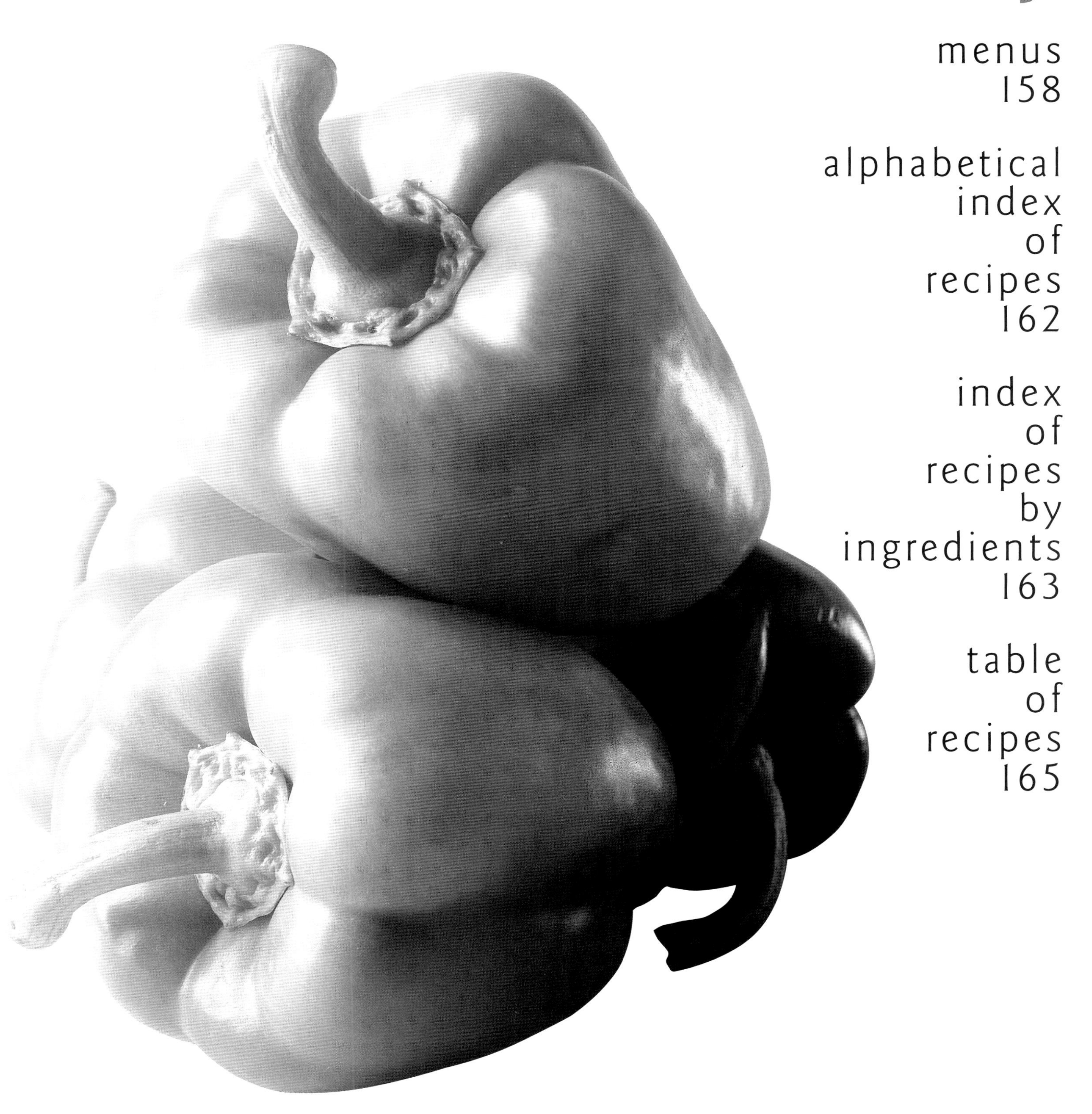

Spring menus

Stuffed courgette flowers

Sea bream with
aubergine purée

Apple flan with
sweet almonds and saffron

•

Prawns with cucumber

Chicken with lemon and potatoes

Grapefruit tart

•

Mussel pilaf

Prawns with red peppers

Peaches with pistachios

•

Citrus monkfish salad

Leg of lamb
with aubergine compote

Olive and aniseed bread sticks
with peach granita

Summer menus

Aubergines with a spoon

Sea bass grilled with fennel

•

'Mille-feuille' of aubergine with crab

Aubergine-wrapped salmon and tomato coulis

Peaches with pistachios

•

Marinated fish

Sardines stuffed with pine nuts and spinach tian

Martine's poached figs

•

Spinach salad with broad beans

Leg of lamb with peppers and spices

Baklava and lemon granita

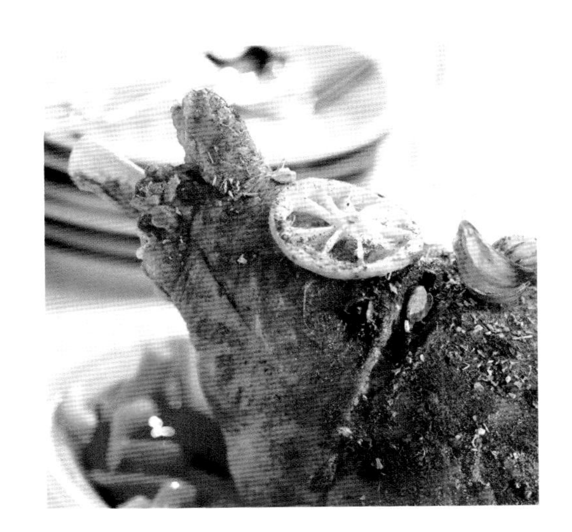

autumn menus

Figs with feta stuffing

Mullet with herbs and
aubergine gratin

Caramelized apples with walnuts

•

Warm tomatoes with goat's cheese

Chicken with thyme crust
and polenta cake

Pears with red wine

•

Mussels with julienne vegetables
and saffron

Quail with cabbage and
juniper berries

Figs au gratin with pine nuts

•

Keftedes

Chicken paupiettes with
goat's cheese and mint

Honeyed yogurt with walnuts

winter menus

Citrus monkfish salad

Poussins with walnuts and
poppy seed crêpes

Pistachio pear cake

•

Cod soufflés with chicory

Maritime leeks

Walnut oil and pine nut cake

•

Scallops in fresh tomato sauce

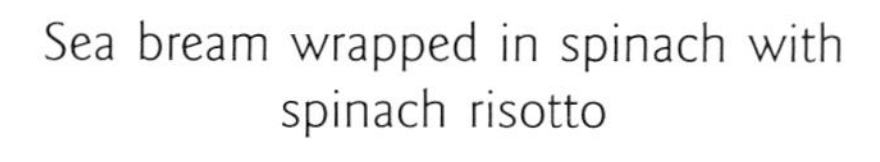

Sea bream wrapped in spinach with
spinach risotto

Andrea's rice

•

Fish soup

Pears with red wine

Alphabetical index of recipes

index of recipes by ingredients

table of recipes

addresses of our friends

Les Diamantaires (Spyros Moissakis)
60, rue Lafayette
75009 Paris
Tél. 01 47 70 78 14

Le Sud (Claude Drigues)
91, boulevard Gouvion Saint-Cyr
75017 Paris
Tél. 01 45 74 02 77

Hôtel Costes (Jean-Louis Costes)
239, rue Saint-Honoré
75001 Paris
Tél. 01 42 44 50 25

Restaurant du Palais Royal (Bruno Hees)
110, Galerie de Valois
75001 Paris
Tél. : 01 40 20 00 27

photo credits

Pierre Hussenot : pages 4, 6, 39 (Sucré/Salé), 41, 42, 44, 46, 51, 52, 54, 57, 60, 62, 67, 68, 72, 77, 82, 85, 87, 90, 93, 96, 99, 102, 107, 110, 114, 116, 121, 123, 126, 128, 129, 130, 133, 137, 138, 141, 143, 146, 151, 152, 155.
Pierre Cabannes : pages 29 (Ryman-Sucré/Salé), 49, 59, 64, 71, 79, 89, 95, 101, 113, 119, 125, 137, 149.
Philippe Asset : pages 24, 26, 27, 28, 30, 31, 32, 33, 36, 38, 46, 61, 76, 81, 83, 84, 88, 92, 94, 104, 117, 118, 128, 132, 134, 135, 136, 139, 147, 153, 154.
Pierre Ginet : pages 26 (blackcurrants, prickly pears, passion fruit, guava) and 32 (tomatoes).
G. Dagli-Orti : page 8, Iraklio, Museum of Archaeology. Minoan Art 1700–1600 BC. Rhyton or vessel for libations, in the form of a bull's head (soapstone, rock crystal), Knossos.
Hémisphères : pages 10 and 11 (bottom), P. Frillet ; p. 12 (top), E. Slatter, P. Frillet, (bottom), F. Guiziou ; p. 13, P. Frillet ; p. 14 (lower left and centre), P. Frillet ; p. 15 (top), E. Slatter ; p. 17 (bottom), F. Guiziou ; p. 21, F. Guiziou ; p. 37, E. Slatter.
Hoa-Qui : p. 10 (upper left), C. Boisvieux, (upper right), B. Perousse ; p. 14 (top), T. Borredon ; p. 14 (lower right), S. Grandadam ; p. 16, S. Grandadam ; p. 17, S. Grandadam ; p. 18 (top), P. de Wilde, (bottom), J. L. Dugast ; pages 19 and 20, N. Thibaut.

Map design page 37 © Hachette Tourisme

Dominique Laty sincerely thanks:

- Spyros Moissakis and his wife Andrea, who together looked for and tested old traditional recipes;
- Claude Drigues, designer and proprietor of 'Le Sud' restaurant, who has carefully followed our project;
- Jean-Louis Costes, who was kind enough to give us the recipe for *Tuna 'costes' and courgette tian*;
- Marie-Sophie Claux, who verified the proportions of the recipes.

Catherine Serbource-Madani thanks the following shops:

Habitat, Ikea, Muji, and *Bernard Carant*. 41, bd des Batignolles, 75008 Paris; *Deux mille et une nuits*, 13, rue des Francs-Bourgeois, 75003 Paris; *CSAO*, 1, rue Elzévir, 75003 Paris; *Sandrine Ganem*, 16, rue de l'Odéon, 75006 Paris; *Homme autour du monde*, 8, rue des Francs-Bourgeois, 75004 Paris; *La chaise longue*, 20, rue des Francs-Bourgeois, 75003 Paris; *Le Bon Marché*, 24, rue de Sèvres, 75007 Paris; *Potiron*, 57, rue des Petits-Champs, 75001 Paris; *Vogica Boutiques*, 91 bd Raspail, 75006 Paris.

The publisher thanks Christine Martin and Marine Barbier for their valuable help and enthusiasm.